Learjets:
The World's Executive Aircraft

Donald J. Porter

TAB BOOKS
Blue Ridge Summit, PA

FIRST EDITION
FIRST PRINTING

© 1990 by TAB BOOKS
TAB BOOKS is a division of McGraw-HIll, Inc.

Library of Congress Cataloging-in-Publication Data

Porter, Donald J.
    Learjets : the world's executive aircraft / by Donald J. Porter.
      p.   cm.
    ISBN 0-8306-2440-6
    1. Lear Jet aircraft—History.   I. Title.
  TL686.L43P67   1990
  629.133'340422—dc20   90-34430
                                               CIP

TAB BOOKS offers software for sale. For information and a catalog, please
contact TAB Software Department, Blue Ridge Summit, PA 17294-0850.

Questions regarding the content of this book should be addressed to:

    Reader Inquiry Branch
    TAB BOOKS
    Blue Ridge Summit, PA 17294-0214

Acquisitions Editor: Jeff Worsinger
Book Editor: Tracey L. May
Production: Katherine G. Brown
Cover Design: Lori E. Schlosser

Contents

Acknowledgments

To Bill Robinson, vice president of corporate affairs at Learjet Corporation, for his assistance in this effort. Also to Don Grommesh, who as chief engineer was a prime mover in the Learjet's design since day one, for verifying the accuracy of much of the material. To Jim Greenwood, retired senior vice president of corporate affairs at Learjet, for his in-depth assistance reviewing the manuscript and his many suggestions to improve its quality and accuracy. To Moya Olsen Lear, Bill Lear's widow, for allowing me access to her personal photo archives. Further thanks to Lilli Locke, administrative secretary to Mrs. Lear. To Dave Pishko of Garrett Turbine Engine Company, for technical information on their TFE331 engines. To Bob Salvucci of General Electric Company, and Douglas Cray of Hill and Knowlton, their public relations firm, for details on General Electric CJ610 engines. "Pete" Peterson and Dee Howard of The Dee Howard Co. provided helpful information on the various Howard high-lift and thrust reverser modifications for the Learjet. And to my wife, Rita Rispoli, for objectively critiquing the manuscript and offering countless suggestions for improving it. Many thanks to each one of you.

Introduction

Mention Bill Lear's name to people who've been involved in aviation for a couple of decades and, more often than not, you'll hear the words ''maverick'' and ''genius'' used to describe this intriguing man. Although he died in 1978, Lear is still revered in aviation circles as nothing short of legendary. More than the inventor of the Lear Jet, he has often been judged as singlehandedly responsible for the acceptance of jet aircraft for business transportation.

In 1950 President Harry S. Truman awarded him the Collier Trophy, aviation's most prestigious award, for his pioneering work in autopilots. But that stratospheric achievement wasn't enough for the man. Unfulfilled by his accomplishments in the aircraft electronics field, Lear had always wanted to manufacture an aircraft of his own design. He envisioned a small, economical jet that could whisk business executives around the country at record-setting speeds. Based on the overall aerodynamic design of the Swiss P-16 jet fighter, Lear commenced engineering work on the executive jet, then designated the SAAC-23, during 1959. In 1962 he moved the project to Kansas, renaming the airplane the Lear Jet Model 23. The plane made its historic first flight the following year. The first production Lear Jet was delivered to a customer in October 1964. Since then, one or more variants of the world's most widely known business jet have been in virtually continuous production.

Lacking the financial resources of his larger competitors, Lear ordered employees to adopt innovative, cost-effective techniques to design and build his executive jet. Whether it was in airframe systems design or FAA certification testing, Lear demanded simplicity in virtually everything designed for the ship. A series of tragic accidents early in the production program marred the airplane's safety record but were later solved, restoring confidence in the jet's design. A record-shattering, around-the-world flight further buoyed confidence in the airplane as production deliveries began to swell.

Following initial production of over a hundred Model 23s, several enhancements of the basic design were produced and culminated in the Model 24. It featured higher gross weight capability, certification to transport aircraft category standards, and a host of other improvements. The Model 25 followed, with a fuselage ''stretch'' to accommodate more passengers.

Victim of an unexpected recession, insufficient cash, and ill-timed corporate diversification, Bill Lear suddenly faced an insurmountable financial crisis. In 1967 he reluctantly sold his interest in the company he had founded only four years earlier to The Gates Rubber Co. Although originally called the Lear Jet, the Gates company soon combined the two words to form "Learjet." Still later, it changed both the company and aircraft names to Gates Learjet.

The late 1960s saw the advent of small, fuel-efficient turbofan engines produced by the Garrett Corporation. The Garrett TFE731 engine soon found application powering a number of executive jet transports, including the Jetstar II, Sabreliner, Falcon 10, and Westwind. Gates Learjet wasted little time in marrying the reliable engine to the Model 25 airframe. The result was the Model 35 and its longer-range cousin, the Model 36. These variants solidly established the Learjet as capable of nonstop transcontinental flight with a low noise level, both in the cabin and around the airport.

In 1977 Gates Learjet announced the big-cabin Model 50 series. Specific aircraft in this series included the Models 55, 54, and 56, with the latter two variants never built. Distinguished by its wing tip winglets, the Model 55 used an upgraded version of the TFE731 engine for power.

In common with the depressed state of the entire general aviation aircraft manufacturing industry, Learjet found itself in a slump during much of the 1980s. Production had slowed to a trickle, but the factory remained open, if only to produce a fraction of its past output capacity. Gates Rubber owned the company until 1987, when it was sold to Integrated Resources. Today, Learjet is once again enjoying renewed vigor and sales activity, delivering the Models 55C and 31 versions.

The corporation producing this now-classic business jet has seen a succession of corporate names concocted by its various owners. In 1962, when Bill Lear was still putting his executive jet concepts on paper, the name of the fledgling organization was the Swiss American Aviation Corporation. When he moved operations to Wichita and started production, the company was named Lear Jet Corporation. Still later, to reflect the diversity he envisioned for the company, it was renamed Lear Jet Industries, Inc. Starting in 1969 the company's new owner, Gates Rubber, titled it the Gates Learjet Corporation, which remained until the company's sale to Integrated Resources. It has since been renamed the Learjet Corporation. At this writing, the company is once again up for sale. The Learjet saga continues.

1
The Great Business Jet Race

Lear Jets. Steam engines for buses. Automobile radios and eight-track stereos. Who hasn't heard of these products? Not known to many, though, is that each of them had its genesis in the mind of an acknowledged genius: the late William Powell Lear, Sr. A common thread runs through the history of each of these inventions: the so-called experts of their day proclaimed each one to be "impossible." Yet Bill Lear routinely proved them all wrong, decade after decade.

Captivated by radio since he learned that the ship *Carpathia* had been summoned via wireless to aid in the rescue of the *Titanic* in 1912, Lear soon became a budding Marconi by building his own wireless receiver. Sensing little need for formal schooling and having little interest in subjects other than radio, he voraciously read the few books he could find on emerging radio technology. Because bonafide "radio engineers" were rare individuals in those days, it didn't take all that much research to gain such a prestigious title. Entering his young adult years, he wanted to be more than a "radio engineer," though. He wanted to be a manufacturer of radio sets.

Surrounded by radio tubes, bits of wire, and leaky jars of smelly chemicals crowded into the musty basement of his mother's home just outside Chicago, Lear's first business venture was called Lear Radio Laboratories. His earliest achievement was developing a new type of radio coil that was only half the size of what radio coils were supposed to be to work properly—or, according to an acknowledged expert in the field of that day, to work at all. A resounding success with the radio manufacturers to whom he sold the coils, Lear changed the name of his company to Radio Coil and Wire Corporation. Pyramiding his beginner's success into something more, he soon traded the fledgling enterprise for a one-third interest in the Galvin Manufacturing Company, a radio chassis manufacturer.

It wasn't long before Lear's small coils made history at Galvin. "These little coils ought to make a nice radio for automobiles," said a visiting engineer. Picking up on the idea, Bill Lear and Paul Galvin set about to make the world's first automobile radios. First, they had to agree on a name for the new product. Galvin suggested a combination name derived from the words "motor" and "Victrola." The car radio was named "Motorola" and Galvin Manufacturing Company became Motorola Incorporated.

Aviation and Electronics Mix Well for Lear

Equally fascinated with radio technology and the barnstormers he had seen flying "ragwings" over Chicago while he was growing up, Lear had already started his ascent in the aviation electronics industry by the early 1930s. He had learned to fly in 1931 after buying a Fleet biplane and tolerating a total of two-and-a-half hours dual instruction before making his first solo flight. Impulsively, he made the flight without his instructor's knowledge. Lear's first cross-country flight later that same year, from Chicago to New York, graphically impressed upon him that pilots of that era spent almost as much time finding out where they were as in getting where they wanted to go.

No sooner Lear had mastered an airplane's controls when he discovered that almost every pilot of the early 1930s navigated by following the railroad tracks winding through the countryside. In trying to sell them aircraft navigation instruments, Lear would ask these independent characters, "What do you do when you reach a tunnel?" or "Which grassy patch in the next town is the airport?" His pitch usually fell on deaf ears. The crusty, self-taught mail and barnstormer pilots resisted aircraft instruments much like ship captains preferred sails even after steam power became available.

Setting up shop in an airport lean-to at the Curtiss-Reynolds Airport northwest of Chicago, Lear designed and produced simple radio receivers and transmitters for the small number of private aircraft owners he had convinced to buy the sets. In addition to their manufacture, he even custom installed the sets in each of his customer's airplanes. Disinterested in the growing airline and military markets, Lear concentrated instead on the independent pilot. He left the huge Bendix Aviation Corporation, RCA, and others to pursue the larger markets. Lear felt at home with private pilots and their simple airplanes. He had found his niche, but the profits didn't materialize as he had hoped. Private pilots either couldn't afford the radios or remained convinced they could get by without them. Even after several years in business, they were still a hard sell for Lear.

Recognizing the void in air navigation capability as a major opportunity, Lear combined his several years of experience in aircraft radio circuit design with the flying knowledge he had gained and invented the Learoscope. The automatic direction finder would use the government's low-frequency airway ranges to help pilots keep track of their location over the ground. He unveiled the Learoscope in January of 1935 with great fanfare, vividly demonstrating the knack for getting the widespread publicity that would be the hallmark of later endeavors in his career. Realizing the importance of getting prominent people to promote his products, Lear convinced World War I ace Captain Eddie Rickenbacker to install a Learoscope on an Eastern Air Lines airliner flying the Miami to New York route. Rickenbacker told the press that Lear's direction finder, which performed flawlessly, was "the most important air navigation aid developed to date."

Bendix Aviation Corporation also produced radio compasses but confined its interest to the more lucrative airline and military markets. Private pilots were small potatoes to such leviathans. Despite the free publicity about the Learoscope and his other products, Lear continued to have a difficult time selling his aircraft radio gear. Even during the mid-1930s, most pilots wouldn't spend their money on aircraft radio equipment when they could still follow railroad tracks. Pilots' attitudes had changed little over the years.

Lear Gets a Big Break

By the late 1930s Lear had developed an advanced automatic direction finder (ADF). With an absence of significant sales to private pilots, he decided to pursue orders from the military, placing him in direct competition with far larger manufacturers. Although his heart was still with private aviation, he knew that the profits his company needed to grow, or even survive for that matter, would have to come from the military establishment.

Lear sought direction finder orders for military airplanes from the Consolidated Aircraft Corporation in late 1940. He walked away without any orders but did land something offering far more potential: a small contract to design and produce electromechanical actuator systems for Consolidated's aircraft. Bill Lear was on a roll. In an amazingly short period of time following the attack on Pearl Harbor, every U.S.-produced aircraft carried Lear Incorporated's electromechanical actuators for operating cowl flaps, bomb bay doors, or anything else that needed to be mechanically positioned. Virtually overnight, Lear's servomechanisms rendered obsolete competitors' hydraulically operated devices. Key to the success of Lear's system was what Bill Lear called the "faststop" clutch. It could disconnect a motor shaft from the device it was driving (such as a cowl flap) the instant the power was shut off. Revolutionary in its precision control, Lear proclaimed that the driven device could "stop on a dime."

Throughout the war years, the company's electromechanical clutches, motors, and actuators formed the basis for the skyrocketing growth and success of Lear Incorporated. The government had become dependent on the company as a key supplier of precision servomechanisms, an essential part of nearly every warplane.

By the end of World War II, William Powell Lear had achieved success in every endeavor. In addition to being a millionaire industrialist, he had accumulated dozens of new patents, molded a company with a workforce of 4,000 employees, and was accorded the international recognition he needed to feed a massive ego. Equipment aboard almost every U.S. military aircraft produced during the war years bore his name. Sales had been good but Lear knew that they could have been even better. The military had also played an insidious game with him, giving innovative product designs to competitors such as Bendix, who later underbid him. His bigger, well-financed competitors had landed lucrative war contracts to produce essentially the same equipment that Lear Incorporated had designed. Trying to circumvent the procurement system as best he could, Lear had fought the military bureaucracy for every dollar of business.

At war's end, Lear's sales to the military dwindled to a trickle. No longer were around-the-clock production lines at Lockheed, Douglas, and Consolidated pushing out thousands of warplanes. The plants were largely shut down, idling hundreds of thousands of aircraft workers. Thousands of planes destined for the war front a year before were now baking in the Arizona sun waiting their turn to be melted down into aluminum ingots. Worsening the picture, an anticipated postwar general aviation boom had yet to materialize.

Needing profits to fuel his ego and his passions, Lear decided to set out in a new direction, seeking to make a dent in the home radio market. Radio was how he had first distinguished himself in the early 1930s; perhaps the market would be kind to him again.

Seeking a change from his original factory location in Ohio, Lear moved to Grand Rapids, Michigan, where he knew a large, eager labor pool existed. Considering the home radio opportunity "simply moneymaking," he left the mundane chore of starting the operation to associates. He immersed himself in the development of new aircraft instruments. The possibility of developing an automatic pilot fascinated him even more. It was a perfect match for Lear; he knew electromechanical actuators and instruments, and autopilots were comprised of both components.

The immediate postwar years continued to prove difficult for Lear Incorporated. Bankruptcy was a constant threat. The moneymaking home radio business soon became a nightmare. Lear had run headlong into massive postwar shortages of materials, and the monopolistic practices of larger competitors were once again creating havoc. In 1948 Lear Incorporated's board of directors disposed of the home electronics operations to stem the spiraling losses.

While Bill Lear tinkered with instruments for private airplanes and a new autopilot, the electromechanical division of Lear Incorporated was generating the cash to pay the bills. It wasn't much cash, though, as the military didn't have much need for Lear's products during peacetime. Lear actuators, screw jacks, and motors continued as an aircraft industry standard, however, as they did during the war years.

Winning the Collier Trophy

Disgusted with the home radio debacle and the monotony of producing actuators, Lear pursued the autopilot project with vigor. Although the military's bomber and transport airplanes had long been equipped with such devices, fighter planes were not. Because fighters carried only a single pilot, Lear reasoned that those ships were most in need of autopilots—particularly the new generation of jet-powered fighters, such as the Lockheed F-80 Shooting Star. Autopilots could provide relief for weary fighter pilots during long flights, allowing them to maintain razor-sharp reflexes in the event of later aerial combat.

Once again combining his knowledge of electronics and aeronautics, Lear began development of a lightweight, three-axis, automatic pilot system for jet fighters. The simple autopilots used on bombers and transport planes of the time had no more capability than keeping an airplane straight and level. They were crude devices when they worked at all, which was seldom the case due to their heavy, leaky hydraulic components. Lear envisioned an all-electronic autopilot, in itself revolutionary, that could actually fly a fighter when the pilot gave the device the direction and desired altitude.

Under Lear's direction, design engineers invented the key component: a special electromagnetic clutch using magnetic particles to precisely position an airplane's control surface actuators. Coupled with newly developed electronic circuitry and gyros to sense the airplane's rate of movement about its axes, Lear was fast evolving an exciting autopilot concept in the company's engineering laboratories in Grand Rapids.

Lear assembled a team of talented engineers and scientists at the Grand Rapids facility. They designed the system by day, and he tested it by night in his own plane. As always, he took personal charge of the testing, installing the prototype unit in his Beech Model 18. With the latest modifications to the prototype autopilot unit installed in the Twin Beech, Lear would take along an engineer to evaluate its performance during late evening flights. Lear also installed the autopilot system in a Lockheed C-60 Lodestar, loaned him by the Air Force for the testing. Maneuvering for hours in frequently turbulent air high over Lake Michigan, the autopilot's performance would be recorded by the two men and minute in-flight control adjustments made to optimize the system's responses.

In 1946 the autopilot project was completed in Santa Monica, California, the new headquarters location for Lear Incorporated. Bill Lear had been intimately involved in every phase of the project from start to finish. By the late 1940s, the resulting all-electronic autopilot was ready for introduction—and large-scale production. It was designated the Lear F-5.

A year's worth of testing by the Air Force was enough to convince the government that the L-5 was indeed revolutionary. In recognition of Lear's pioneering autopilot work, President Harry S. Truman presented him with the prestigious Collier Trophy in 1950, aptly described as "the Pulitzer Prize of aeronautics." Further recognizing his achievement, the University of Michigan bestowed an honorary doctorate in engineering on the genius who never finished high school. The degree acknowledged "the advances which your inventive genius has made possible in modern methods of communication and aviation."

Autopilot laboratory at Lear Incorporated's Michigan plant during the late 1940s. This room was the birthplace of the L-5 autopilot, which won Lear the Collier Trophy. Moya Olsen Lear collection.

The innovative L-5 autopilot created a genuine stir in Air Force circles. Weighing only about a quarter as much as older, far less capable systems, it was hailed as revolutionary, even by Lear's worst skeptics. No other autopilot came close to its performance. At last, Lear had beaten Bendix and Sperry at their own game. The Korean War that soon followed provided an unexpected bonanza for Lear: the military equipped its F-84 and F-86 jet fighters with the F-5. America's first spy plane, the U-2, was later equipped with it, too.

Lear's intuition in pursuing development of the F-5 was a smart move for Lear Incorporated. The company garnered production contracts worth almost a billion dollars over the ensuing 12 years.

Bill Lear's interest in the utilization of autopilots went farther than the autopilots themselves. He took particular interest in the gyros that supplied critical aircraft attitude and directional information to the autopilot system. If this angular information wasn't accurate under all flight conditions, the autopilot couldn't do its job properly. Whenever an aircraft entered a turn or changed its speed, the resulting unwanted accelerations would affect the accuracy of ordinary gyros. Spending many an evening in Lear Incorporated's gyro laboratories, he helped develop a vertical gyro system that would not be adversely influenced by accelerations of the aircraft. Lear Incorporated's work on such gyro devices was again recognized as outstanding by the government, with every U.S. combat aircraft in the Korean conflict being equipped with Lear vertical gyro indicators.

The F-5 triumph now behind him, Lear again slipped into boredom and restlessness. He had mastered the aviation electronics field, but what next? Because his first love was still airplanes and flying, developing an actual airplane would become his next challenge.

Bill Lear inspecting an autopilot installation aboard a heavily instrumented Twin Beech during the 1950s. Moya Olsen Lear collection.

The Learstar Evolves

Restless for opportunity, Bill Lear finally tired completely of making the military electromechanical actuators and radio gear that his company had produced for decades. "It's just plain old moneymaking," he would be fond of saying. He wanted more of a challenge, something that would involve him directly in flying. Not surprisingly, Lear Incorporated's board of directors and plant managers felt the same. Without an all-consuming interest, Lear had become an annoyance to plant management, interfering with the autopilot and instrument production lines and interrupting workers to make changes that weren't allowable under the company's government contracts. They wanted him out of their hair.

Lear often flew the vintage Lodestar he obtained from the Air Force for use as an autopilot testbed. The more he flew it, the more he became intrigued with making minor aerodynamic modifications to the airplane. Each time his mechanics modified a wing or control surface or installed flush rivets, the Lodestar's performance perked up a bit more. He discovered that the airplane's speed and climb performance could be raised without increasing the engine power.

By the mid-fifties, Lear was ready to make his part-time Lodestar hobby a mainstream business. He convinced the board of directors of Lear Incorporated to establish an Aircraft Division, which would buy up old Lodestar hulks (from Lear himself), modify them to Lear's exacting specifications, and resell them as "Learstar" executive transports. The fact that Lear wouldn't have time to interfere with autopilot production because of the Learstar was reason enough for the board to grant him his wish.

To bring the production Learstar to fruition, Lear hired Gordon Israel, an irascible but erudite engineer, who had gained notoriety during the thirties by designing a number of winning racing airplanes. Self-taught, much as Lear was, Israel had been designing jet fighters for Grumman Aircraft before the company fired him because of a drinking problem. Lear also hired Ed Swearingen, a talented designer who years later went on to bring the world the Merlin and Metro series of turboprop business and commuter airline aircraft.

The production Learstar was a highly modified Lodestar, with major changes in the airplane's wings, tail, and systems. Powered by two Wright R-1820 nine-cylinder radial engines, the ship featured a bevy of Lear Incorporated instruments and radios as standard equipment. Luxury carpeting and leather seats, combined with unprecedented speed and range, quickly established the Learstar as the preeminent piston-engine executive transport of the day.

Lear wasn't alone in the modification game, though. Other competitive conversions of World War II airplanes emerged, including the larger 18-cylinder R-2800-powered Howard 500, Super Ventura, and On Mark B-26; but it was tough for them to compete with the Learstar's ideal size, performance, and luxury. Lear had succeeded in raising the Lodestar's cruise speed from 220 to 280 miles per hour and its nonstop range to 3,800 miles—all without increasing the engine power. Described by one of its test pilots as a "real bullet," it was the fastest twin-engine transport, with the longest range, then in production. Pilots had to fly the airplane to believe its impressive performance reputation. Even Lockheed's famed design genius, Clarence L. "Kelly" Johnson, who had designed the original Lodestar almost two decades earlier, didn't believe that Lear could raise the old ship's level until he saw it for himself.

The first Learstar took to the air from the Santa Monica Municipal Airport on May 10, 1954. Nine months later, the Civil Aeronautics Administration certified it as complying with all airline transport safety standards. In February of 1955 the first production ship was delivered to a Canadian oil company. Staffing up for what he thought would be large-scale production, Lear hired hundreds of skilled engineers and production workers, centralizing the work in a large hangar he had leased at the Santa Monica airport.

Bill Lear (left) in the cabin of his Learstar during the 1950s. Standup headroom and roominess of the converted Lodestar are evident. Moya Olsen Lear collection.

Unfortunately for Lear, the ship's $650,000 price tag became the principal obstacle to its long-term success: only 60 of the ships were sold before production was terminated. The Aircraft Division, with the Learstar its only product, had not been profitable for Lear Incorporated. With the exception of Lear, the board was unanimous in its feeling that the company's aircraft manufacturing venture had created an unconscionable cash drain.

The board sold the Aircraft Division, with its Learstar program, to Pacific Airmotive Corporation. The drastic action left Bill Lear without a plaything. For the time being, he concentrated on refining the company's line of avionics and instruments for business and airline aircraft. His attention to this endeavor didn't last long. He finally relegated the day-to-day management of Lear Incorporated to his key executives and in 1959 retreated to Geneva, Switzerland, a favorite spot, to design an all-new executive aircraft.

Lear Gambles on a Jet for Business

From its inception, Lear had viewed the Learstar program as the first step toward designing and mass producing his own high-performance executive aircraft. While working on the Learstar, his engineers made preliminary sketches of different configurations for an all-new, six-passenger executive airplane. Lear Incorporated's board of directors had resented his using company funds to work on what appeared to be personal projects (such as paper airplanes). Now resettled in Geneva, he could concentrate on developing his revolutionary airplane design without the interference of his meddlesome board. Lear remained Lear Incorporated's absentee board chairman and principal stockholder.

Sensing an unprecedented opportunity, Lear went about sketching what would eventually become the Lear Jet. Jet transportation had arrived, and he reasoned that few executives would care to continue traveling in the discomfort of a piston airplane after enjoying the silky smoothness of a ride in the new Boeing 707. If he could be the first to design, certify, and produce a compact, affordable jet, he could corner the market for years to come. Termed an iconoclast by peers, he was alone in this conviction. Lear felt he'd have little competition because of the skeptical attitude of rival aircraft manufacturers. He was confident that the business flying community was ready for such an airplane.

Even while the last few propeller-driven Learstars were rolling off the Santa Monica conversion line, two major aircraft manufacturers within 20 miles of Lear's hangar were hard at work on a totally different type of executive airplane: the light jet transport. In 1956 the U.S. Air Force had indicated interest in procuring a number of lightweight twin-jet transports. Powered by turbojet engines, the airplanes would be used to transport senior military personnel, civilian VIPs, and high priority cargo. North American Aviation responded with a twin-jet design known as the NA-265 Sabreliner. Awarded a contract in 1956, the company began development of the jet. In March of 1957 Lockheed Aircraft Corporation announced that it was also developing a light utility jet transport, offered in response to the Air Force's Light Utility Transport (LUT) program. Lockheed's new transport would be called the L-1329 Jetstar, later designated the C-140 by the Air Force. Originally powered by two turbojet engines, the Lockheed airplane would sport four smaller Pratt & Whitney turbojet powerplants in its production version.

The prototype Sabreliner first flew on September 16, 1958. In October of that year, the Air Force placed a quantity order for the aircraft, by now designated the T-39. The U.S. Navy soon followed with another order. Procurement of the Sabreliner would eventually total 200 ships.

The late fifties saw the world's airlines moving rapidly into the jet era. Boeing 707s and Douglas DC-8s were fast replacing piston-powered DC-7s and Super Constellations, and the military was already shuttling its brass around in military versions of the Sabreliner and Jetstar. Only the world of business aviation seemed to be ignored by aircraft manufacturers during this new jet age. Although North American and Lockheed had introduced civil variants of their military light jet transports, their price tags were far beyond the reach of most corporations. The board chairmen of Fortune 500 corporations were still dodging thunderstorms in World War II vintage Twin Beeches, Lodestars, DC-3s, and, yes, even Learstars. While children and elderly ladies were streaking effortlessly through the stratosphere in tourist class aboard 707s and DC-8s, these titans of American business were lucky to reach the same destination in twice the time. Recognizing the edge that an airline's jets had over the archaic lineup of piston business aircraft, some executives were actually selling their corporate airplanes and once again flying the new commercial jets. "Time is money," they'd say. Unless the exodus from business aircraft ownership could be reversed, it would mean the end of the postwar business flying boom. Business aviation provided independent mobility and the capability to slip into almost any airport, but it lacked the jet speeds now offered by the airlines, and in the final analysis, an executive would always opt for greater speed.

The First Designs

The early months of 1959 saw the first designs for the Lear Jet emerge from the drawing boards in Geneva. The preliminary design concept was based on the Marvel, a U.S. Army research aircraft built by Mississippi State University. It was powered by a single Allison T-63 turboprop engine driving a shrouded pusher propeller. The same engine, in a turboshaft version, would eventually find its way into the U.S. Army's OH-6A and OH-58A light observation helicopters.

Featuring seating for six, the Marvel was built of a molded fiberglass airframe structure with the lightweight Allison engine mounted at the aft end of the fuselage, adjacent to the propeller. The prop itself rotated inside a six-foot diameter shrouded ring built into the tail structure. It was the Marvel's performance that aroused Lear's attention: it could fly up to an amazing 350 miles per hour. According to industry observers, it was probably the most efficient subsonic airplane ever built.

Bill Lear had wanted for years to design a pusher prop airplane, and he liked what he saw in the Marvel. Dr. August Raspet, head of the Marvel design team, met with Lear in April 1959 to discuss the Marvel's technology. Raspet offered Lear his recommendations for a twin-engine turboprop pusher with the propellers located inside similar six-foot ringlike enclosures on the tail. The Allison turboprop engines would again be mounted on the tail, eliminating the need for long propeller driveshafts.

This "new" Lear-produced Marvel would cruise at 344 miles per hour at 25,000 feet, featuring a range of 1,520 miles. Lear called it the Lear Pusher Turboprop Airplane. This design was officially designated the Lear Model 59-3, referred to as the "Eight Place Executive Airplane Twin Turbofan." There was one big change, though: this design had two turbofan engines located on the tail in lieu of the earlier turboprops. The Lear Jet concept was born.

During the summer of 1959, Lear negotiated with Mitsubishi, a major contractor for F-104 jet fighters built in Japan under license from Lockheed. He wanted to handle the engineering and prototype testing of the new ship and then sell the design to Mitsubishi for production. The airplane would be called the Lear-Mitsubishi Executive Transport Aircraft. After a year of stalemated negotiations, the talks broke down. Lear was back where he started.

In the meantime, Lear's oldest son, Bill Jr., had been running Lear Incorporated's sales and service operations in Switzerland. He had also become a fan of a new Swiss fighter-bomber called the P-16. Bill Jr. knew that the P-16 was a sturdy ship and had a wing design very close to what his father wanted for his own business jet. The P-16 was designed by Dr. Hans Studer and manufactured by Flugund-Fahrzeugwerke Altenrhein (FFA). This company had built four P-16s and later lost two of them in crashes over Lake Constance. The company had originally set out to sell the P-16 to the Swiss Air Force. With the loss of half its fleet, it looked like the end of the line for the P-16.

Dr. P. Caroni owned FFA and asked Bill Jr., whom he respected as a discerning pilot, to test-fly the P-16. The younger Lear found the airplane to have outstanding flight characteristics. Wasting little time, Bill Sr. hired Studer to transfer the P-16's aerodynamic features to a corporate jet. Forming the Swiss American Aviation Corporation, Lear called his new design the SAAC-23.

Designing the SAAC-23

Lear moved his newly formed company to St. Gallen, next to the FFA factory in Altenrhein. By mid-1961 basic design work on the SAAC-23 had begun. Lear's objective was to keep the SAAC-23's weight under 12,500 pounds so it would qualify for single-pilot operation under FAA CAR 3 regulations and for air taxi operations without requiring CAB approval.

At the same time Lear was getting started, Aero Commander of Bethany, Oklahoma, announced that they were developing another executive jet, to be called the Jet Commander 1121, powered by the same General Electric turbojet engines that Lear planned to use on the SAAC-23. Always enjoying a good fight, Lear knew that the SAAC-23 would run into competition from the Sabreliner, Jetstar, Jet Commander, and even the smaller four-place MS-760 Morane Saulnier marketed by Beech in North America under license from the French manufacturer. He dismissed the threat of the far more expensive Sabreliner and Jetstar, designed expressly for the military, calling them ''royal barges.'' With only four seats, the French-built Morane Saulnier was too small, and the Jet Commander would be larger and slower than his own dream jet. Not unlike the unfair game that major electronics manufacturers such as Bendix had played with him during the war, it was Lear's turn to monopolize an industry: the business jet market. The right airplane was all he needed.

Preliminary design calculations showed that the SAAC-23 would offer a 500-mile-per-hour cruise speed, 600-mile-per-hour maximum speed, 2,000-mile range, 6,000-foot-per-minute rate of climb, and a 45,000-foot maximum ceiling. It would be delivered completely equipped for a $500,000 price tag. Most important to Lear, the SAAC-23 would be a true ''pilot's airplane.'' Every inch of the new plane would feature what Lear, as a longtime businessman-pilot, felt was important in an executive transport.

Lear wanted an airplane that would better the speed and comfort of the 707 or DC-8. It would replace the existing fleet of medium and heavy piston-powered twins converted from airline use to transport executives. The aging DC-3s, Convairs, Martins, Lodestars, and Twin Beeches could be relegated to the boneyard.

FFA would assemble the prototype in Altenrhein and build the first few planes. The initial plan was for FFA to do the tooling and make the wings and wing tanks in Altenrhein; Heinkel in Germany would make the fuselage and tail; and Thommen of Switzerland would make the hydraulic components and undercarriage. Alcoa would supply the sheet metal; General Electric, the CJ610-2B jet engines; BF Goodrich, the brakes; and Lear Incorporated, the jet's flight and navigation instruments.

Lear optimistically predicted sales of more than 600 SAAC-23s, basing his forecast on the decentralization philosophies of many American corporations in locating manufacturing plants away from the big airports of major cities. Increasingly, corporate executives had to rely on their own aircraft to get to the plants. Few smaller airports in the 1950s had scheduled airline service. If they did, a businessman would probably get stuck on a slow-moving DC-3. Lear's jet would provide corporate management with a viable solution to their plant visit dilemmas.

The Swiss were excited over Lear's plans—the Swiss Federal Air Office promised to expedite Swiss certification and cooperate with the FAA to certify the SAAC-23 at the same time. The prestige and profitability of Lear's proposed project would certainly benefit Switzerland's economy.

Optimism in Switzerland and Trouble in Santa Monica

All the time that Lear was relishing his stay in Switzerland developing the SAAC-23, Lear Incorporated continued to function without its absentee chairman. Company insiders said that the business ran better because Lear was not around to "meddle;" but Lear was soon to face troubles in his corporate board room. The SAAC-23 was originally intended to be a "private" personal project of Lear's, but the board uncovered that he had tapped into some of Lear Incorporated's corporate resources, getting him in hot water with several board members. Lear had played the same spending game years earlier with the Learstar project, expending company funds on personal pursuits. He had also "borrowed" some of Lear Incorporated's brightest engineers to assist with the executive jet project. This time the board was stern in its pronouncement: enough was enough. It wanted nothing to do with the risky business jet project. The capital needed to design, certify, and start up production of such a jet could kill the company. The new airplane would be in direct competition with some of the company's biggest customers, and other than transforming runout war-weary Lodestars into shiny Learstars, the company had never built a single airplane. Nor did it want to. The vivid memories of the money-losing Learstar fiasco figured heavily in the board's decision to turn the project down. It wanted no further siphoning of the company's resources to fund Lear's pet project.

Making a series of ardent appeals to the board to fund the executive jet project, Lear was solidly turned down. Disgusted with the board's inability to visualize the future of business aviation and his project, he decided to sell out his entire stock holding in Lear Incorporated.

When the Siegler Corporation indicated to William R. Staats, one of Lear Incorporated's board members, an interest in exploring merger possibilities with the Lear company, Staats tipped off Lear. Negotiations between the two companies were soon to follow. When they concluded, Bill Lear had sold his 470,000 shares of Lear Incorporated for $22 each, totalling $10.3 million. Also sold were another 100,000 shares set up in a trust fund for his children, which brought in $2.2 million more. Lear's total shares amounted to 27 percent of the corporation's stock.

The merged companies became Lear-Siegler, Inc. and remained headquartered in Santa Monica. Other than a loose association with the new corporation as a temporary "consultant," Lear had severed all ties with the company he had founded decades earlier; however, he would be allowed by Lear-Siegler's board to retain the right to call his new airplane the "Lear Jet." Bill Lear and his paper airplane were now on their own.

Pressure to Make Progress Grows

While work on the SAAC-23 continued in Switzerland, business jet competition loomed on the horizon. In January of 1962, France, Dassault, and Sud-Aviation were starting to build the prototype fanjet-powered Mystere 20 (later redesignated the Falcon). Larger and more expensive than Lear's design, it would still contribute to crowding the marketplace that much more. Lear felt pressured to make faster progress. He appointed his trusted right-hand man, Buzz Nanney, as general manager of the SAAC-23 program. A former detective on the Los Angeles police force, Nanney had become associated with Lear during the 1950s while moonlighting for him doing security work around the Santa Monica plant. Although not especially knowledgeable about aircraft design or manufacturing, Nanney did know how to keep a project progressing along the right path. Lear needed that ability: he had promised the world's aviation press and prospective customers that his new jet airplane would fly within a year.

To get things moving, Lear brought in Gordon Israel, who had been chief engineer on the Learstar, as a design consultant. Unfortunately, the hard-driving Studer and abrasive Israel couldn't work together. Both men had strong, unyielding personalities. During the Learstar's heyday, Israel had sometimes not shown up at work for days on end. He had a longstanding drinking problem, of which Lear was well aware. When Israel finally did meet up with Lear at the Santa Monica hangar, both men would shout at each other, the arguments ending with Israel walking off the job or temporarily getting "fired" by Lear. In spite of its volatility, it was a productive relationship.

Attempting to break the stalemate that was crippling engineering progress, Nanney hired Hank Waring as chief engineer in mid-1962. Waring had been chief engineer at Cessna, responsible for developing the Model 320 twin, T-37 jet trainer, and other Cessna designs. The situation didn't improve: Waring, Studer, and Israel now argued among themselves. However, Waring did bring along a handful of talented associates to proceed with the work, including Don Grommesh, who would later become chief engineer.

Although the SAAC-23's airframe was taking shape nicely, little work had been done on its all-important systems—electrical, hydraulic, and instrument. Years earlier in a magazine interview, Lear had half-jokingly said that he wanted an "abundancy of redundancy" in his new jet. This meant that the airplane's electrical, hydraulic, and pressurization systems would be duplicated or even triplicated; but the work going on in Switzerland showed little attention to such details.

Lear had never liked the work ethic of the Swiss, which he considered sluggish and inefficient. It seemed as if the smallest increment of progress took forever. "Grab the job and run with it" was more his style. He wanted action, yet the leisurely ways of his Swiss employees seemed to block his efforts.

The Big Move

Responding to his concerns about the Swiss work ethic, Waring convinced both Nanney and Lear that it would be best to move the operation to the United States. Perhaps somewhat biased because he came from Cessna's Wichita plant, Waring recommended locating the Lear plant in that Kansas city. Wichita was the acknowledged aircraft manufacturing capital of the midwest. In fact, city fathers had nicknamed it the "Air Capital of the World." Not wishing to absorb any more costs caused by another relocation blunder, Lear decided on an unbiased objective approach to the relocation decision. Making a methodical relocation analysis, unorthodox for him, staff members evaluated Cedar Rapids, Iowa, Dayton, Ohio, and Wichita, Kansas. All indicators pointed to Wichita. Concurring with the survey, Lear chose that midwestern city in the heart of America to spawn his brainchild.

In retrospect, Wichita was lucky to get Lear. At the time, its major aerospace employer, Boeing, was laying off people. The city had become overly dependent on fat military aircraft contracts. Continuing to benefit from old line general aviation manufacturers Beech and Cessna, the city council knew all too well that it had done little to entice new firms to locate in Wichita. They knew that Lear's new plant could put thousands of the city's unemployed aircraft workers back to work; however, because the iconoclastic Lear had never gotten along well with the general aviation aircraft establishment, specifically Cessna and Beech, he had few other allies in Wichita. Never having manufactured a single aircraft from scratch (the Learstar was a "conversion"), Lear wasn't taken too seriously, except by a small number of Wichita's civic leaders who were smitten with the fact that "flying people were with him. He was the underdog."

At the June 1962 Reading Air Show in Pennsylvania, Lear displayed a small cockpit mockup of his airplane. In aviation circles, Reading was considered "the" trade show for business aircraft manufacturers. A good showing there had raised many a company from oblivion to prominence. However, the mockup wasn't much of a presentation for a company that steadfastly argued that it was going to revolutionize executive air transportation. A short distance away, a full-size mockup of the Jet Commander was on display. North American and Lockheed were flying and actively selling their plush, million-dollar aerial limousines, but Bill Lear had something that the other companies didn't: indomitable spirit. He was a pilot, a respected member of the business flying fraternity. His track record with the Learstar and the superior autopilots he had developed over the years sat well with his colleagues. Corporate pilots and aircraft owners knew him, felt comfortable with him, and believed what he promised about the Lear Jet.

Although Lear had done much to bring about the business jet era, there was little doubt that he was now starting to look like the underdog in the competition to build that airplane. No longer neck and neck in the race, he was falling behind the others.

The decision to move the fledgling SAAC-23 project from Switzerland to Kansas involved shipping 500 tons of equipment to Wichita. While Buzz Nanney cleaned up the

Full-size cockpit and cabin mockup of the original Lear Jet, circa 1962. Moya Olsen Lear collection.

ensuing legal mess brought about when Lear severed his contracts with Caroni in Switzerland, Lear began setting up shop in Wichita.

Providing the right financial incentives to lure Lear, the city of Wichita offered to raise $1.2 million in industrial revenue bonds for Lear's new plant. It would be built on a 64-acre cornfield next to the city's municipal airport. For working capital, Lear borrowed $7 million from the Bank of America. He secured the loan with a note for $10 million, proceeds from the sale of his Lear Incorporated stock. The $10 million represented practically all of his personal wealth. He had put every dime on the line. The bank needed collateral because every aircraft industry leader in town had assured the banks that this man, with no major aircraft manufacturing experience (except that of a "converter") and only an eighth-grade education, could never pull off such a grandiose feat. Putting his money where his mouth was and ignoring such detractors, Lear hired an architect to design the newly named Lear Jet Corporation's plant. The SAAC-23 airplane itself was renamed the Lear Jet.

Lear's architect designed a 96,000-square-foot building that sat on the edge of the airport adjoining a new taxiway built by the city. It would be capable of assembling ten airplanes at a time. Driven by Lear's constant pressure, the contractor built the plant in only five months. It was an immense challenge to build such a big complex during the subzero weather of a Kansas winter, but with other business jet competitors lurking on the sidelines, Lear needed to get rolling immediately. The contractor was forced to pour concrete over the former cornfield and erect the hangar's massive steel trusses under biting cold conditions throughout the fall and winter of 1962. Completing the plant during such inclement weather and within so short a time frame was a major Lear Jet milestone and an accomplishment in itself.

On January 7, 1963, Bill Lear and a minuscule workforce of 75 employees moved into the new buildings. He promised to roll out the first Lear Jet by June of that year. Lear knew he had the jump on the "big three" of general aviation—Cessna, Beech, and Piper. None of these companies had yet moved to produce an executive jet, all of them skeptical of Lear's efforts. His only direct competition was the Jet Commander designed by Ted Smith, a general aviation design luminary who later developed the Aerostar series of light twins. Lear knew that he was in a neck-and-neck race with Aero Commander's new jet. Powered by the same 2,850-pound thrust General Electric CJ610 engine that would power the Lear Jet, the prototype Jet Commander took to the air for the first time on January 27th from the airport at Aero Commander's Bethany, Oklahoma, plant. Lear had a lot of catching up to do and not much time to do it.

Doing It on a Shoestring

Pressed for time and having only $12 million to design, fly, and certify the airplane, Lear had no choice but to skip the customary step of making a prototype. Instead, he would move directly to the production phase. The prototype tooling, built in Switzerland, would later serve as production tooling. The first "prototype" would actually be a production airplane, available for later sale. Aircraft manufacturers would occasionally resort to this method of development when one of two situations surfaced: they didn't have much money or they had so much faith in the aircraft's design that few changes to the prototype were expected before production. Bill Lear knew that he couldn't enjoy the luxury of either changing the first design much or building a dedicated prototype. He just didn't have the money to do those things.

Settling into the cavernous new plant with his skeleton workforce in the dead of winter, the Kansas winds howled across the airport's runway. Not one to waste time on pleasantries, Lear hammered into everyone's head his personal Lear Jet design philosophy. It was his airplane and every design detail would have to satisfy him alone. Everything would be kept as simple as possible, as long as safety was not compromised. This meant leaving out "unnecessary" components and equipment. "If you leave it out, it can never break down," Lear would be heard saying while bent over a drawing board.

The original Lear Jet Model 23 is an unusual airplane in that it represents the ideas and design philosophy of a single person. Bill Lear's imprint is to be found in virtually every component and system aboard the airplane. In stark contrast to today's "committee" system of designing aircraft, Lear's almost dictatorial management style ensured that his final product would represent exactly the airplane that he felt would be the right one for the business aircraft market. Whether it was the size and shape of the seats, slope of the windshield, or location of a single switch, Lear's desires prevailed without exception.

Birth of the first Model 23 occurred on February 2, 1963, when assembly of the ship's airframe began from already fabricated airframe subassemblies. Throughout the spring months of 1963, the airframe was "stuffed" with wiring harnesses, plumbing, and control systems to turn the shell into a completed airplane.

The business jet race had now enlarged to include the foreign competitors. The first flight of the twin-turbofan powered Dassault Mystere 20 was made in France on May 4. Much larger than the Lear Jet, the aircraft would appeal to customers desiring a larger, walkaround cabin. Feeling encroaching pressure from the Jet Commander, Mystere 20, and still other proposed jets, Lear "pounded on his boys" to get the first Model 23 finished. On June 7th the first fuselage structure left its jigs, heralding the start of the final assembly effort for the first ship.

Early 1963 were busy months in the Lear Jet hangar. Listening to the advice of his latest chief engineer, Don Grommesh, Lear ordered that the horizontal stabilizer be moved up to the top of the rudder, above the wing's slipstream. Earlier, Gordon Israel had urged Lear to do the same thing. It would provide more stability and prevent possible future metal fatigue. It also gave the airplane a more rakish look than before, which couldn't hurt sales any. Earlier in the month, the forward and aft fuselage sections were mated. On August 16, the wings and fuselage were joined together. The first Lear Jet was finally in one piece.

Not enjoying the much larger financial resources of his competitors, Lear was forced to rely on unconventional methods to certify his jet. A good example was the locally built water tank used to test the fuselage's pressurization. The complete Model 23 fuselage was pressurized with air to its normal operating pressure and submerged in the tank to check for leakage. Other manufacturers traditionally used a complex hydraulic system to pump water in and out of the fuselage to conduct such tests. But Lear didn't have the time or the money needed for that method. Time had truly become money to him now, and he was running out of both.

Rollout and First Flight!

On September 15, 1963, the first Model 23 was rolled out from the Wichita hangar. Less than a month later, on October 6th, the ship was ready to fly, except for a minor problem with the nosewheel assembly. During taxi tests, the wheel would caster sideways when the brakes were applied. The solution was found to be minor, with Lear and his technicians fixing the problem later that night.

Late afternoon of October 7 saw Lear Jet Model 23 801L roar down Municipal Airport runway 32 under the control of test pilot Bob Hagen, its crackling GE turbojets propelling the small ship into the chilly Kansas air for the first time. It was almost dusk. In another few minutes, the flight would have had to be canceled because of darkness. Wichita had never seen anything like this: over a thousand spectators lined up a dozen deep alongside the runway. The entire city had followed Bill Lear's progress in developing his jet on an almost daily basis. Most of the town's citizens shared the spirit and undaunted hope he had maintained during its hectic development. Many of the spectators were Lear Jet employees, taking their few precious hours off work to watch history in the making. Still others knew that if the airplane sold, they could be Lear Jet employees in the near future. Even a few skeptics from the front offices of the old-line Cessna and Beech plants were there.

Henry (Hank) G. Beaird, Lear Jet's chief test pilot, took turns at the day's piloting duties with Bob Hagan. Beaird was a former fighter pilot, having test-flown F-105s and F-84Hs as chief experimental test pilot at Republic Aviation. Hagan was formerly

Prototype Lear Jet Model 23, N801L, takes to the Wichita skies for the first time on October 7, 1963. Note "experimental" placard in cabin window. Moya Olsen Lear collection.

Cessna's chief of flight tests for the T-37, 310, and 320 airplanes. For days before the flight, Beaird continually battled Lear, who wanted to make the first flight himself. While he had faith in the Lear Jet's design, Beaird told him that first flights can be dangerous. He rattled off a list of airplanes that never made it beyond their maiden flights, and he sternly pointed out to Lear that if he lost his first airplane, he could build another. But if he lost his life as the Lear Jet's first test pilot, that would be the end of the entire Lear Jet Corporation. The merits of Beaird's argument grudgingly sank into the chairman of the board's head: Bill Lear would watch the first flight from the safety of his Lincoln Continental parked alongside the runway. A two-way radio would allow him to keep constant contact with the flight crew.

Swooping low over the runway with Beaird at the controls, N801L made a faultless approach and smooth landing at the airport where it all began. Hundreds of hands clapped as the main gear tires chirped, hitting the runway pavement. The first airplane flew well, Beaird saying that "Lear Jet Corporation has itself one hell of an airplane." Both pilots pronounced the first flight as outstanding in every way. Predictably, there were a lot of tears around the airport that eventful afternoon. The city's faith in the project had been reaffirmed. Lear's lenders were relieved. Wichita's aircraft workers no longer doubted that Lear would be hiring thousands of people just like them.

A big party at the nearby Diamond Club celebrating the event came later that night. The talk among the crowd was that the "stormy genius" would now take over the business jet race and revolutionize corporate air transportation. Once the hangover from the party wore off, Lear's crew had their work cut out for them. The Aero Commander people had made their first flight on January 27, 1963. He now had to expedite the FAA certification process as much as possible. He had to make up for lost time—a task that Bill Lear was always good at.

Lear Jet 801L had flown over 50 flights by the end of January 1964. The airplane had been flown to speeds as high as .905 Mach, or 699 miles per hour. With dozens of successful test flights of 801L logged to assess the airplane's flying qualities and systems performance, the first flight of the second Model 23 took place on March 5th. Other than minor changes and modifications, no changes were required of the Model 23 airframe or systems. On April 1, Bill Lear started official efforts to gain FAA certification for the Lear Jet. May 15th saw the first flight of the third Model 23.

Moving into the thick of the FAA certification process, FAA inspectors could be found inundating every inch of the Lear Jet hangar, examining the most minute details of the airplane and its engineering documentation. Lear put the pressure on the regional FAA office handling the certification paperwork to speed things up, but to little avail. Angering the regional people, he went over their heads, shouting his dissatisfaction directly to FAA Administrator Najeeb E. Halaby during a telephone call. "Save your dime, I can hear you without the phone," Halaby is reported to have said.

While engineering development of the airplane was encountering essentially simple technical problems, Bill Lear's fledgling enterprise was running out of money. Having spent all of his own and the bank's money, he had also spent the deposit money collected from customers for future Model 23 deliveries. Appealing to Lear Jet distributors to sell more airplanes and raise more deposit money, several of them together came up with an additional $310,000. The money became a lifesaver.

The Crash That Became a Blessing

Tragedy lurked around the corner on June 4, 1964: the first Lear Jet built, N801L, crashed during a routine test flight required for FAA-type certification. A seemingly experienced FAA jet pilot, Donald Keubler, had absent-mindedly failed to retract the airplane's wing spoilers while attempting a takeoff from the Wichita airport to evaluate the jet's single engine performance. The airplane couldn't gain enough altitude above surrounding terrain and pancaked into a nearby cornfield in what could only be described as a "controlled crash." Coming to rest, the airplane was largely intact, with both pilots uninjured; but no sooner had they exited the airplane when a fuel line broke, spewing fuel on hot engine parts. In another second, Bill Lear's first airplane erupted into flames. Spotting the thick, black smoke spiraling upward from the cornfield beyond the runway, Lear suspected that the worst had happened: his airplane had crashed. In another minute, he was to find out he was right. Within a few more minutes, only a charred heap of aluminum remained of N801L.

Under any other circumstances, Bill Lear would have been unbelievably upset. The loss of a prototype airplane almost always meant the collapse of an aircraft development program, but this situation was uniquely different. Lear was delighted: the insurance money he would collect for the loss of 801L was what he needed to keep Lear Jet Corporation afloat. At this point, the money was more important than a single airplane.

Word of the crash spread like wildfire throughout the aviation industry. Rumors abounded that the airplane mysteriously fell out of the sky killing everyone aboard. Jim Greenwood, Lear Jet's public relations man, advised Lear that there was nothing more important at the time than taking the second ship, originally destined for Lear's friend, Justin Dart, to the Reading Air Show, which was running at the time. Greenwood warned Lear of the consequences should their competitors continue to spread vicious rumors about the Lear Jet's integrity. The second ship was being used for certification testing before delivery to Dart. Without hesitating, Lear pulled it abruptly out of its test role to make the impromptu visit to Reading. He had to show the business flying community that he was still in business. Streaking into Reading with his only remaining Lear Jet, he was ushered into an airport room packed with reporters for what could be the most important news conference of his career. The tactic worked; Lear told the gathering all the details of the accident and retained the respect of the business aviation community. He even pulled in more prospective customers. Said Greenwood: "Our news briefing made lemonade out of a lemon."

With the insurance money in the bank to meet the payroll and supplier bills, Lear Jet Corporation was very much still in business. Together with nonsafety concessions made by the FAA concerning the Model 23's certification timeframe, (brought about by their embarrassment that an FAA pilot crashed the airplane), Bill Lear was once again on a roll.

FAA Certification at Last

July 31, 1964, was a jubilant day around the Lear Jet Corporation plant—the Model 23 was awarded FAA type certificate A5CE. It took 253 flights of the second airplane to prove the airplane's credibility to the FAA. Taking a day off from his Washington duties, Administrator Halaby flew to Wichita to present the Model 23's type certificate to Bill Lear. It had been the fastest FAA approval of a new design in history, less than 10 months from first flight to type certificate. According to Lear himself and a few people within the FAA, much of the credit for the fast action was due to Lear's constant prodding of the FAA bureaucracy.

With a type certificate in hand and a new factory waiting to produce airplanes, Lear activated the production line immediately. The mountain of debt and little working capital gave him no choice. He needed the cash from a string of sales to keep the struggling company operating. On October 13, 1964, two and a half months after Halaby handed Lear the airplane's type certificate, the first production airplane was delivered to Chemical and Industrial Corporation of Cincinnati, Ohio. It was the third Model 23 off the assembly line.

With delivery of the first Model 23 now history, those aircraft manufacturers who had taken the earlier position that "no market" existed for business jets were starting to eat crow. Perhaps the most beautiful civil airplane ever to grace the skies, the Model 23 was unlike anything else in the world, and its performance equaled its looks. Six passengers could now be comfortably whisked across the country at speeds up to 540 miles per hour, above the weather at 41,000 feet. The Model 23 would become the progenitor of a line of airplanes that would symbolize the words "business jet" for a long time to come.

However, gaining the FAA certification victory had almost killed the company. Bill Lear's $10 million was gone, along with the additional millions he had borrowed from the banks. Years later, history would record that Bill Lear and subsequent owners of the company bearing his name would experience a continuum of financial gyrations while making their business jet the biggest seller in the world.

William P. Lear posing for a publicity shot in front of his soon-to-be-famous brainchild. Moya Olsen Lear collection.

2
A Quarter-Century of Ups and Downs

Autocratic, frequently unreasonable, and unpredictably insulting are a few of the traits in a boss that most employees would prefer to avoid. To an employee in any other company, a single one of these verbal abuses might be reason enough to quit working for such a tyrannical boss. At Lear Jet Corporation, similar treatment by Bill Lear was routine rather than an exception. It had always been the way he had managed his enterprises. The behavior was tolerated by employees who were entranced by the vision, courage, and energy of their chairman of the board in building the most revolutionary business aircraft to come about in decades. Everyone at Lear Jet Corporation was making history, and more than anyone else, Lear himself knew it.

Whether it was Lear Incorporated or Lear Jet Corporation, Bill Lear's management style was the same. Amazingly, the results he obtained differed markedly from what a human relations textbook may say on the subject. Sometimes ridiculed and demeaned by Lear, people still believed in the man, sticking with him through thick and thin. When Lear Jet's treasury ran low in 1965, many employees went down to half-salary and doubled the time put in at the plant. Sundays and nights were routine. If Lear was at the plant (which he almost always was), his "boys" would be there, too.

If history were to record a fervent, almost fanatical dedication to a boss, Lear's reign as an industrialist would surely top the list. Lear was a visionary. His indomitable drive enabled him to communicate that strong vision. He loved to prove people wrong when "they said it couldn't be done." One of the lucid biographies chronicled about Lear took the liberty of using that phrase as its title. The other half of his success can be ascribed to his considerable staying power. His bursts of energy kept the vision moving swiftly to fruition. Regardless of the odds against him, Lear wouldn't give up, exemplifying the quintessential American entrepreneur.

While Lear was at the helm of Lear Jet Corporation, it was one of those companies that assumed the colorful personality of its founder. Described as a "stormy genius" by many associates and underlings, Lear could often be found on the production line long after plant closing time. Having utter contempt for the corporate committee decision-making process, he would instantly change what he didn't like—usually without the approval or concurrence of anyone else in the company.

"Put up half the money and you can make half the decisions," Lear would say to those who wanted more of a voice in the decision-making process. Employees who had been entrenched in corporate bureaucracies for years found the situation either refreshing or distressing. Some found Lear's directness and candor an ideal way to get things done. Others quit in disgust, blaming him for making all the decisions and not taking full advantage of the talented staff he had at his disposal. "This guy is a one-man show," they'd complain.

As he did with the Learstar back in Santa Monica years before, Lear would sketch a modification out on the back of a napkin or envelope, march straight into the shop to put the part together, and rush into the hangar to fit it onto a production Lear Jet. Reminiscent of Lear Incorporated, his actions left production operations in chaos. Years earlier, Lear was effectively barred from the production floor at Lear Incorporated for the same reason.

Going Public Fills the Coffers

Much as he did during the war years, Lear knew that the way to raise the capital he needed to push ahead with Model 23 production was to sell his corporation's stock to the public. It's not that he had much choice: both he and his company were fast running out of working capital. Not only would it provide the desperately needed cash, but it would return Lear to his former millionaire status.

On July 30, 1964, Lear Jet Corporation applied to the Securities and Exchange Commission (SEC) to sell its stock to the public. Precariously perched on the edge of a financial debacle while he awaited blessing from the SEC, Lear pleaded with employees to take deep pay cuts in return for generous stock options he would provide them when the company went public. Not surprisingly, their deep loyalty to him won out: all but a few agreed to stay on, recognizing the potential of the Lear Jet program. It was obvious to them that if Lear himself invested every dime he had into the project, the project must have merit. For months, Lear worked with his underwriter, Van Alstyne, Noel and Company, and the SEC in gaining the necessary approval to sell stock to the public.

On November 30, Lear Jet Corporation became publicly owned. Bill Lear had sold 550,000 shares of his own Lear Jet stock for $10 a share. After the stock offering, he still retained 60 percent ownership, remaining president and chairman of the board. The company used proceeds from the offering for various purposes. About $2.5 million was used as working capital, $1.5 million helped reduce the company's outstanding debt, $1 million bought more tooling and manufacturing machines, and half a million doubled the factory floor space. Lear paid all back salaries and gave out the stock options he had promised employees during the financially lean months preceding the offering.

Lear's marketing plan for the airplane divided the country into six sales regions, a distributor being appointed for each region. He didn't pay nearly as much attention to such marketing matters as he should have, however. Firmly believing he had the best "mousetrap" in the world, Lear convinced himself that customers would forever continue to seek his product out, getting in line to pay a premium price for the ship. In time, that marketing strategy (or perhaps the lack of a strategy) proved to be fatally flawed. Domestically, a network of franchised distributors was appointed from coast-to-coast, but few of them had much experience in selling an airplane as sophisticated and costly as the Lear Jet. In Europe, Africa, and the Near and Middle East, Bill Lear, Jr's Executive Aviation Corporation in Geneva became the exclusive distributor. Each distributor paid $50,000 for a franchise and profited from a five percent discount for every Model 23 order they obtained. The agreements called for customers to commit a $50,000 deposit at the time they made a purchase decision; an additional $100,000 when the plane went into production; $125,000 when they were notified of the mating of the wing and fuselage; and the rest of the $550,000 purchase price upon delivery. Anxious customers readily agreed to the terms.

Lear Finds Time to Tinker

Consumed with developing his new jet during most of his workweek, which routinely included Saturday and Sunday, Lear still found time to continue working with the electronic devices he loved to tinker with. Together with longtime associate Sam Auld, he had a hand in developing many of the avionic devices that found their way into the Model 23: flight instruments, electronic black boxes, and, of course, the autopilot. Along the way, his fertile mind also came up with the concept for a new tape player for automobiles. Up to the time, four recorded tracks on a quarter-inch tape were considered by audio industry experts to be the maximum attainable. Lear set out to prove the rest of the world wrong again. The small tape cartridge player developed by the two men, suitable for installation in a car, contained a compact tape cartridge having eight separate audio tracks. Pencil in one hand and soldering gun in the other, Lear toiled during long Wichita evenings designing the device and fabricating a prototype in Lear Jet's shops. By the fall of 1964, Lear and Auld had a tape player that worked better than anything else then available. They were ready to "take the world by storm" with it.

In April of 1965, Lear Jet, Ford, and RCA announced a deal they had worked out between them. Ford would offer Lear Jet's stereo player in its top-of-the-line cars, and RCA would offer a wide variety of prerecorded music cartridges. Bill Lear was ecstatic. He was the first to introduce stereo tapes for the new car market and the first to offer an eight-track stereo. Commercializing the unique product idea, Lear formed the Stereo Division as an extension of Lear Jet Corporation. Following its embryonic days in Wichita, the Stereo Division was relocated to Detroit, Michigan, in a 54,000-square-foot building on February 19, 1965. As was normal for him, Lear had lost interest in the stereo shortly after he invented it. The eight-track tape player was now relegated to the status of merely another obscure division and moneymaker for his now burgeoning corporate empire.

The Darling of the Jet Set

"One day Bill is having lunch with a king, the next day he's flying somewhere with a movie star," recalls a former Lear Jet manager. The natural charisma that made dedicated zealots out of Lear Jet employees also made true believers out of customers. The Model 23 was fast becoming the darling of not only corporate America but also the Hollywood jet set. Frank Sinatra was one of the first to become a Lear Jet owner, stepping up from a Twin Beech. Other entertainers were also quick to become Lear Jet converts, trading in their now-archaic propeller-driven airplanes. Good friends and aviation buffs Danny Kaye and Art Linkletter could be seen frequently roaming around the plant, flown in by Lear himself. Having learned to fly a few years earlier, Kaye became so enthusiastic over the airplane that he became a Lear Jet vice president. Another friend, Justin Dart, multi-millionaire head of Rexall Drug and Chemical Company, had ordered the second production airplane off the assembly line. Recognizing Lear's fast accelerating financial debacle, he paid cash in advance for the airplane to aid the low working capital situation at the company. With Dart's okay, the airplane was diverted for FAA certification testing when Lear's prototype crashed. After Dart took delivery of a later ship months later, tragedy struck again. The airplane was flying in turbulent air miles over the Texas plains when it mysteriously crashed with a company pilot and FAA check pilot aboard. In spite of the catastrophe, Dart never failed to offer unwavering support for both Lear and his businessman's jet. Bill Lear's strong alliances and loyalties in the business aviation community, as well as entertainment and political circles, were paying off.

The Model 23's sleek, racy looks earned it a prominent position on the covers of dozens of aviation magazines around the world. Publicity about the Lear Jet was without precedent in the aviation press. Braving the heat of summer and snowstorms of winter, reporters hounded the Wichita plant for news about Lear, the airplane, or even what celebrities had flown in the ship lately. Wherever Lear went, the press wasn't far behind. Much to Bill Lear's liking, the Lear Jet was fast becoming legend. While much of the credit for the onslaught of publicity could be attributed to the airplane itself, Lear made it clear to reporters that he personally deserved the credit. If it wasn't for him, there wouldn't have been a Lear Jet at all, of course. As he had done with every product of his since the Learoscope, Bill Lear knew what it took to get the all-important publicity the company needed to get the orders to fill its financial coffers.

Because every Model 23 manufactured featured an array of Lear's own avionics and instruments, the avionics manufacturing operations were mushrooming. Almost all of the sales were made to equip Model 23s flowing off the Wichita assembly line. The products included remote attitude and directional gyros (which were built around surplus World War II gyro units), electric nosewheel steering controls, and a new lightweight autopilot based on the components Lear had used years earlier on the F-5 system. Rather than reinvent the wheel, Lear was fond of repackaging old ideas and components to obtain improved performance. With Sam Auld at the helm, he decided to set the avionics company up as a separate, fully functioning division in a location where plenty of space and an experienced engineering workforce were available. He had been a leading aircraft instrument supplier when he owned Lear Incorporated and wanted to regain that prominence. Doing without a corporate relocation survey this time, he established Grand Rapids, Michigan, as the location for the new headquarters of the Lear Jet Avionics Division, on December 30, 1965. Of course, he was no stranger to Grand Rapids, having enjoyed much of his postwar industrial success there. He knew the town well, and Grand Rapids embraced his return.

Too Much Too Soon

Placing most of his energy in getting Model 23s off the assembly line, the company's customer service operations had taken a back seat to the manufacturing department and had suffered from the start. Finding enough experienced service personnel, particularly electricians, was a seemingly perennial problem. To quench the pressing need for the same kind of people for Lear Jet manufacturing operations, newly hired workers would be shuffled into manufacturing. Although customer service may have been ignored in the rush to get airplanes out the door, Lear knew that the long-term success of the airplane would depend on the level of technical support his company provided customers.

Responding to these concerns, he announced the third major expansion of the Wichita plant on February 1, 1966. Highlight of the expansion plan was a totally integrated customer aircraft service center, bringing total factory floor area to 400,000 square feet.

Unwisely seeking to diversify before achieving solid profitability with the Lear Jet itself, the company's board of directors authorized the purchase of a 97-percent ownership interest in the small Brantly Helicopter Corporation of Frederick, Oklahoma, in May of 1966. At the time, Brantly was manufacturing two models of light piston-powered helicopters, the two-seat Brantly Model B2B and the four- or five-seat Model 305. Lear viewed those models as merely steppingstones to adapting the turbine engine to an all-new helicopter. He foresaw a fast twin-engine, turbine-powered helicopter for business— a rotary wing equivalent of the Lear Jet. Not wanting to delay development of the new helicopter, Lear immediately hired a number of well-known helicopter designers, including Harvey Nay, to put a design on paper. Largely ignoring the company's rapidly worsening cash drain, Lear spent considerable money on the jet helicopter project until later forced to abandon it when the corporation started teetering on the brink of bankruptcy.

By June, Lear Jet Corporation's sales topped 120 airplanes; but trouble was brewing. With little warning, the sales suddenly stopped cold—eight jets sat unsold on the Wichita ramp baking in the summer sun. The country's economy had reached the top of the business cycle, slipping down into a recession. As corporate flight departments are traditionally the first expense that corporations cut back on during lean times, the recession immediately took its toll on new aircraft sales. Corporate controllers were saying "no" to purchases of expensive new business aircraft like the Lear Jet. Congress had earlier aggravated the sales decline, discontinuing the seven percent investment tax credit that had made purchases of large capital equipment, such as business airplanes, very attractive to corporations. With little tax incentive, corporate treasurers were now downright nervous when it came to investing in airplanes.

Lear Jet Corporation wasn't alone in its dilemma: every other general aviation aircraft manufacturer shared a similar fate. Wichita's aircraft plants, including rock-solid Cessna and Beech, were now seeing canceled orders, and workers were being laid off. However, these major manufacturers enjoyed more staying power to weather the downturn. Unlike them, Lear had been operating with too little cash almost from the start and now desperately needed more Lear Jet sales to stay afloat.

Despite little cash in bank, and ignoring the uncertainty blatantly obvious to others, Lear continued his expansionary push for the company. July of 1966 saw groundbreaking ceremonies for a 50,000-square-foot building in Grand Rapids to house engineering and manufacturing operations for the avionics division. The division was continuing to build avionics for the Model 23 as well as other aircraft, although these other sales continued to be meager.

In September, the board of directors changed the company's name from Lear Jet Corporation to Lear Jet Industries, Inc., reflecting the diversification efforts underway. The company's board, driven by Lear's insistence, had wrongly assumed that the expansion would help cure its economic ills, when in fact it merely exacerbated them. The company was mired in deep financial quicksand and sinking fast.

The Big Downslide and Rescue

The company that manufactured the fastest-selling business jet in the world was now losing money. At the same time corporate pilots were anxiously awaiting the day they might be lucky enough to be at the controls of a Lear Jet, Wall Street analysts were awaiting the firm's demise. Poor marketing of the Model 23 and the company's overzealous overdiversification were two big reasons for the woes. Whatever profit was generated by the Aircraft Division was instantly gobbled up by the other cash-hungry components. Lear's distributor system was proving ineffective in selling expensive jet aircraft, resulting in the inability of the factory to enforce sales territories and prevent price-cutting tactics, which resulted in lowered profits for everyone. Most of the small distributorships had never sold an executive aircraft in the Model 23's price class before, and they were continuing to show that they were just not up to the task.

Bill Lear now faced the inevitable: either shut the company down until the economy picked up or sell out his ownership to another company or an individual having the financial resources to weather the recession. Money would have to be pumped into advanced models of the Lear Jet that the marketplace was demanding. Grudgingly, he chose to sell the company.

Soloing an open cockpit biplane as a teenager in 1928, Harry B. Combs had built a virtual empire in the general aviation fixed base operation business. Based in Denver, Combs was the largest distributor in Beechcraft's history. Still later, seeking to slow down a bit during his advancing years, he sold out his interest in Combs Aircraft to The Gates Rubber Company, also based in Denver.

Gates Rubber was headed by Charles C. Gates, whose father had bought the Colorado Tire and Leather Company in 1911. The elder Gates made only one product—a steel studded leather sleeve that slipped over automobile tires. The Gates Rubber Company grew from those humble origins. Known for its conservative, financially solid management, the firm manufactured a broad line of rubber products for the automotive and industrial markets, including tires, V-belts, and radiator hoses. A pilot himself since 1942, Gates was an ardent aviation enthusiast engrossed with aviation's future potential. In addition to buying Combs Aircraft, Gates had also acquired Roscoe Turner Aeronautical Corporation in Indianapolis, Indiana. He operated both as large general aviation fixed base operations.

Although semi-retired following the sale of his FBO company to Gates, Combs took on a temporary role as a consultant to Gates, advising him on aviation matters. He had followed the Lear Jet saga closely. It wasn't long before Combs told Charlie Gates that the company was in trouble and might be a a good buy, primarily because of its future potential. Respecting Combs credibility, Gates and Combs toured Lear Jet's Wichita facilities together. Both men liked what they saw.

Sensing the potential for a deal, Gates asked Combs to analyze the company's financial and marketing situation. Combs put together a turnaround business plan from which they determined it was viable to make an offer for the troubled company. He had known for a long time that the company's primary problem was ineffective marketing caused by the weak distributor network that Lear had originally organized. Combs came up with a plan to surmount that shortcoming and operate the company profitably again. Satisfied with what he saw, Gates contacted Lear and negotiations between the two men followed quickly. Again disregarding the impending financial downfall of his company, Lear maintained a hard line in the negotiations, demanding the price for his shares that he felt appropriate. Not wanting to lose this perhaps once-in-a-lifetime opportunity to buy the company, Gates agreed to Lear's terms, and a deal was struck.

On April 10, 1967, Gates Rubber took over controlling interest in Lear Jet Industries, Inc. Bill Lear stepped aside as chief executive officer, relinquishing those responsibilities to Charlie Gates. However, Lear did remain a member of the company's board of directors. "This is a major step in Gates Rubber's long-range plan to contribute to the general aviation industry," a company news release said. "It also serves to reinforce the company's financial stability and depth of management for the growth years ahead."

The soft market that Lear had encountered lingered, not improving all that much later in the decade. There were more than a few times when Gates had wondered if his purchase of the company might have been a colossal mistake, but he remained committed to doing all he could to bring the company out of the doldrums. Six months after Gates took over, the elongated Model 25 was introduced. It was the financial shot in the arm that the struggling company needed. Learjet Industries, Inc.'s annual report for 1968 reported net sales of $34.6 million. Reflecting the nagging problems that caused Lear to sell the company, a net loss of $4.6 million was also reported. A year later, with the new Models 24 and 25 stacking up new sales records, sales had edged up to $58 million with net earnings of $2 million. The only unprofitable operation in the company continued to be the Stereo Division.

On May 1, 1968, the Avionics Division became Jet Electronics & Technology, Inc. (J.E.T.), a wholly owned subsidiary of Lear Jet Industries, Inc. Headquarters remained in Grand Rapids. Later that same month, Lear Jet Industries acquired Avsco, Inc., a leading producer of plastic products. It too became a wholly owned subsidiary. Making a further commitment to customer service, a new aircraft service center was opened in June of 1968 to double customer service facilities in Wichita. Seeking to convert all operating divisions of the corporation into wholly owned subsidiaries, the Stereo Division became still another subsidiary of Lear Jet Industries, Inc. On October 1, 1968, it became known as Lear Jet Stereo, Inc.

The wisdom and velocity of the changes occurring at Bill Lear's namesake were too much for the founder to remain passive much longer. He had moved to Reno, Nevada, to pursue another challenge: developing steam engines for cars and buses. Whenever a board meeting was called, though, he'd fly his personal Learjet back to Wichita. When he got there on each visit, everything seemed a lot different than it used to be. He didn't like what he saw.

Although chairman of the board, he held what was in effect merely a title, with no real power to implement his own ideas. The decisions of the board were collective ones; Lear's outspoken opinions were essentially ignored. He was now but a single cog in a wheel. Adding to the unpleasantness, his relationship with Charlie Gates had become strained. Lear was impulsive and restless, and he shot from the hip. Gates was methodical, analytical, and perfectly content to analyze operations with computer printouts. Following each meeting, the chasm between the two grew wider.

On April 2, 1969, William P. Lear, Sr. resigned as board chairman of Lear Jet Industries, Inc. His resignation was accepted without comment by the other corporate directors during a routine board meeting. Bill Lear had now completely severed his remaining ties with the most important company he had ever founded. He had also left behind any official ties with the airplane that revolutionized executive air transport.

The shareholders of Lear Jet Industries, Inc. ratified an agreement and plan of reorganization on December 2, 1969, which made Gates Aviation Corporation a wholly owned subsidiary of Lear Jet Industries. Gates Aviation had replaced Learjet's ineffective distributorship network when Charlie Gates assumed control two years earlier. Since that time, Gates Aviation had added a sales and service operation in Palm Springs, California, in addition to the two FBOs already operating in Denver and Indianapolis. To sell new airplanes where Gates Aviation facilities weren't located, Gates Learjet maintained four regional sales offices around the country. The shareholders also approved changing the name of Lear Jet Industries, Inc. to Gates Learjet Corporation. The airplane itself was redesignated the "Gates Learjet."

The last year of the tumultuous sixties saw Gates Learjet post record earnings of $2.4 million, but it wasn't long before trouble crept in again. Caught in the grips of still another recession, skittish treasurers were tightening corporate purse strings. Capital equipment, such as executive airplanes, were again the first things on the budgetary chopping block. As a result, the airplane's sales took a nosedive, and the company racked up whopping losses; but slow Learjet sales weren't the only culprit. In 1971, practically all of Gates Learjet's red ink came from Lear Jet Stereo, Inc. Bill Lear's brainchild, the revolutionary eight-track stereo player he had invented only a few years earlier, was continuing to lose market share to the newer cassette types of players.

New Leadership at the Helm

The depressing financial news did nothing good for morale around the factory. It didn't take long for friction to develop between Malcolm S. Harned, Gates Learjet executive vice president for engineering and manufacturing, and G.H.B. "Hig" Gould, Gates Aviation executive vice president for finance and marketing. When Gould started merger talks with Northrop Corporation during 1970, Harned became infuriated and resigned. On October 16, 1970, the company's board of directors hastily made Gould president of Gates Learjet, replacing Gates who already had too much else to do. Gates remained chairman of the board. The Northrop negotiations eventually went nowhere, but Gould later conducted merger talks with other possible suitors. Gould had assumed responsibility for a company that seemed to be bleeding to death: it was operating in the red with its airplane sales plunging downward.

Irrespective of the recession, deliveries of new Learjets made during 1970 increased the number of airplanes delivered to customers to near 300. It marked the sixth year in a row that Gates Learjet had led all business jet manufacturers in the total number of airplanes produced.

On April 30, 1971, Charlie Gates was forced to resume the duties of the presidency of Gates Learjet Corporation, following the untimely death of G.H.B. Gould in a Denver automobile accident on April 23rd. Within days of Gates taking over the reins again, Gates Learjet's organization was streamlined to include only aviation-oriented operations. Combs had urged him to take the actions. Lear Jet Stereo, Inc., Avsco, Inc., and the Static Power Division (a spinoff from the avionics division) were purchased by The Gates Rubber Company, leaving Gates Learjet to concentrate on aircraft manufacturing, marketing, and service functions. The fixed base operations and Jet Electronics & Technology, Inc. remained as Gates Learjet subsidiaries.

Most of the news lately wasn't very encouraging. Gates Learjet needed some good news. On October 6, 1971, it got it: the company was presented the Presidential "E" award by the U.S. Department of Commerce. The award cited the company's performance in export sales, which totalled over $50 million since the first international sale was made by Bill Lear back in 1965. A day later, Harry Combs, already a Gates Learjet board member, was elected president of Gates Learjet Corporation. He replaced Gates, who had been serving in the arduous dual role of president and chairman of both Gates Learjet and The Gates Rubber Company since April 30, 1971.

Owing to its slippery, slow flight characteristics, particularly on approach, along with its high speed, thorough flight training had always been an all-important concern at Gates Learjet. Responding to this need, FlightSafety International, Inc., one of the world's largest and most prestigious pilot training organizations, established a training center at Gates Learjet facilities in Wichita. Announced on January 6, 1972, the facility offered recurrent Learjet flight training, along with pilot and mechanic ground school. This was the first time a business aircraft manufacturer and an independently owned flight training organization had merged their expertise, placing their operations under the same roof. Heart of the FSI training center was a Gates Learjet flight simulator. It realistically simulated practically any in-flight maneuver (normal or emergency) that the airplane might encounter.

The herculean managerial efforts expended by Combs, and an economy that was starting to help and not hinder sales, paid off by 1972. On June 26, 1972, a record net profit of $8,654,000 on consolidated sales of $59,256,000 was reported by Gates Learjet Corporation for the fiscal year, "climaxing one of the most dramatic financial turnarounds in the industry's history," a company news release said. A record 90 purchase orders for Learjets had been received during the company's 1972 fiscal year. These included 49 domestic and 41 foreign orders. All of the company's operations, including aircraft manufacturing, fixed base operations, and J.E.T., were profitable for the year.

On January 7, 1973, Gates Learjet observed the 10th anniversary of opening the first factory building in Wichita. For the eighth consecutive year the company had led the industry in the sale of business jet aircraft, now having made approximately 360 total deliveries. Gates Learjet's three fixed-base operations in Denver, Indianapolis, and Palm Springs were officially consolidated under the name Comb-Gates a month later.

The Learjet fleet, now comprised of some 470 aircraft, topped the 1,000,000 flight hour mark in September of 1974, becoming the first business jet type to achieve this distinction. By January 1, 1975, with a total of 479 airplanes delivered, Gates Learjet had, for the tenth consecutive year, continued to lead the business jet industry in total aircraft delivered.

Ideas Sprout in Reno

Following the sale of Lear Jet to Gates, Bill and Moya Lear retreated to Beverly Hills, and then to Reno to contemplate their future. No sooner had he arrived in Reno did Bill Lear embark on a number of new ventures. Not content with a single enterprise, he formed Lear Motors Corporation, Leareno Development, and Lear Avia. Lear Motors would design and produce engines for cars, buses, and boats, all powered by steam. The company was also working on a brushless electrical motor and battery recharger. The Leareno company owned over 5,000 acres of land adjacent to Reno's Stead airport, which Lear envisioned developing into a major commercial and residential "planned community." While all this was going on, engineers at Lear Avia were hard at work designing a new autopilot, yaw damper system, jet engine sound suppressor, helicopter muffler, and a new highly efficient "supercritical" wing for jets, particularly the Learjet. All the enterprises were headquartered in a cluster of austere buildings at the Stead airport, just north of Reno's bustling metropolitan area.

Typifying his style, Lear had too many projects on his plate without enough money to fully develop any of them. The steam engine project consumed millions of Lear's dollars. In the end it fizzled out without producing a dime of profit. Lear spent the bulk of the money he received from Gates on the steam project before finally abandoning it. Testing had shown that it wouldn't be practical or economical enough for such an engine to be mass-produced. At about the same time, Lear's five-year noncompeting agreement with Gates Learjet had expired, allowing him to pursue work on still another business jet design. Disgusted with technologies he knew little about, such as steam engines, he felt far more at home with airplanes and aviation developments.

The result of his preliminary efforts to design still another business jet was the Learstar 600. What distinguished it from other contemporary airplanes was its NASA-developed supercritical wing, which would provide unprecedented long range and an unusually slow landing speed. The airplane would be powered by two new Lycoming ALF 502D high bypass ratio fanjet engines. In his heart, Lear wanted to design and manufacture the new jet himself, but the bitter realities of his financial plight soon relegated that thought to the sidelines. Without the millions he had back during the startup of Lear Jet Corporation, the best he could do now was to design the ship and have someone else manufacture and market it. Through an intermediary, Lear cautiously approached the licensing of his pet project to a likely prospect, Canadair Limited of Montreal.

In April 1976, Canadair bought an option for $375,000 to produce the Learstar 600. The deal would also provide Bill Lear with advances paid against future royalties on the Learstars that the Canadian manufacturer would build. Not long after signing the agreement, he brought aboard old hand Sam Auld to run Lear Avia and Leareno, while Lear himself spent all his time working on the Learstar's design. Not surprisingly (in view of the number of projects Lear had started), Auld found a mess in Reno. He immediately began to stem the cash flow drain, selling off or discontinuing unprofitable projects.

No sooner had the hard-driving Lear started working with the Canadians than trouble erupted: the Canadair people weren't listening to him. After a series of major disputes, Canadair drastically modified Lear's original design, expanding the fuselage cross section. Lear sarcastically called it "Fat Albert." As a final insult, Canadair renamed the ship Challenger 600, effectively shutting Lear out of its development.

Effectively divorced from the Challenger's development, but still drawing advances against royalties from future deliveries of the jet, Lear directed his energies to the final aeronautical project of his life, the Lear Fan. By June 1977, the Lear Fan design was taking shape. It would be the first all-composite passenger airplane ever built and the first mass-produced airplane having only pusher propellers.

Development of the Lear Fan was chaotic, with constant turmoil among the design staff and changes in its basic configuration. Confident in the Lear Fan concept, Lear continued to pour the Canadair advance money into its development. Aside from two flyable prototypes, the first making its maiden flight on January 1, 1981, the Lear Fan project was never completed. Much of the spirit behind the project died when Bill Lear did, on May 14, 1978. The Lear Fan wasn't even remotely ready for the marketplace. Moya, Bill's widow, made a valiant attempt to keep the spirit alive for several years, but the project ultimately went bankrupt in 1985. Only the two flyable prototypes were built, along with one static test unit.

The Challenger 600 eventually became a best seller, offering a new standard of stand-up headroom and long range for corporate air travelers. It joined the Gulfstream II as a Rolls Royce of corporate jets.

The Expansion Continues

In 1975 with a very tight labor market in Wichita, the local aircraft manufacturers started looking at other locations in the western U.S. to expand, anticipating a continuing growth of general aviation. Gates Learjet executives searched the west, ultimately settling on Tucson. Following negotiations with the Tucson Airport Authority (TAA), the company eventually built 578,919 square feet of plant space on 163 acres it had leased from the TAA. The Tucson facility opened in 1976 with an aircraft completion center, the first of a number of buildings to be erected on the site. At first, airplanes in the "green" configuration were ferried to Tucson for finishing and delivery. Later, component parts for the ships, such as airframe sections and fittings, were manufactured in Wichita and shipped to Tucson for assembly into finished airplanes. Customer service and other production operations were added in progressive stages, augmenting Wichita's capabilities and capacity.

Many business jet manufacturers were delivering their aircraft in a "green" condition to customers—that is, unfinished both inside and out, and with the characteristic green exterior color of zinc chromate primer. Gates Learjet's Tucson operation offered customers factory "custom completion" services to paint the airframe, design and outfit interiors, and install custom avionics in the airplanes.

Through 1975, total cumulative Learjet deliveries had reached 570, making it the 11th straight year that Learjets had topped the business jet industry in total deliveries. Reflecting the good financial news generated by the sales, a 10 percent stock dividend, the first ever paid by the company, was announced for payment on March 18, 1976.

During the 1975 fiscal year, a record 93 new airplanes were delivered. The total included an industry record of 21 airplanes delivered just in the month of April. One of these was the 600th ship built, a Model 35A. It went to Dart Industries, founded by Justin Dart, the man who had paid cash in advance for the second Lear Jet off the line in 1965 to help a struggling Bill Lear succeed.

On April 15, 1977, Gates Learjet marked its 12th consecutive year as an industry leader, having delivered a total of 655 business jets since 1964. Enjoying such success with its products, the company's financial fortunes also swelled. The board initiated the first cash dividend ever declared by Gates Learjet Corporation: 10 cents per share. It was announced to the company's shareholders on July 29, 1977. On the same date, 4,303,885 shares of company stock were owned by about 5,500 shareholders. The delivery of 105 airplanes during calendar 1977 established still another industry record and increased to 760 the total number of Learjets delivered. It was the corporation's 13th consecutive year of leadership in cumulative business jet deliveries.

Tucson's hangars continued to run at full capacity. The rapidly expanding worldwide fleet dictated still more space for customer service facilities to provide the level of support that the company's sophisticated customers were demanding. A 44,000-square-foot, $1 million customer service center was completed at the Tucson facility in April of 1978. It complemented the capabilities of Tucson's custom completion facility, now in full-scale operation. This newest service center brought to 20 the number of centers making up the worldwide network of authorized service facilities.

A record $243,080,000 in consolidated sales with net earnings of $9,839,000 was reported for the fiscal year ending April 30, 1978. Sales were up 24 percent from the previous year and profits rose 29 percent. For the 14th consecutive year, Gates Learjet led in worldwide cumulative business jet deliveries, having delivered 102 in 1978, hiking to 862 the total delivered to date.

During November of 1978 FlightSafety International established a 10,000-square-foot Learjet training center at Gates Learjet's Tucson facility. This center augmented the similar facility operating since 1972 at the Wichita plant.

March 28, 1979, saw the 1,000th airplane delivered. The customer was the Eaton Corporation, a leading manufacturer of high technology products, located in Ohio. This was Eaton's sixth Learjet, which made it the largest Learjet corporate fleet in the world.

In February of 1980 Combs announced an expansion plan, exceeding 200,000 square feet, to be devoted to still more customer service facilities. Included in the plan was a new $5.2 million hangar and office complex in Wichita and a $2 million facility in Tucson. Business was booming, and the increasing number of airplanes comprising the worldwide Learjet fleet dictated steady growth in after-sale service capabilities. The delivery of 120 new Learjets during 1980 set an all-time company record. In the company's 15th year, more than 1,000 airplanes had entered worldwide service, exceeding the production of the company's nearest competitor by more than 300 ships.

When the large-cabin Model 55 was ready for production, the decision was made to manufacture the entire airplane in Tucson. Formal ceremonies were held in Tucson on April 30, 1981, to deliver the first production Model 55 (serial 55-004) to a retail customer, Transcontinental Gas Pipe Line Corporation, of Houston, Texas. The Model 55 was the first Learjet ever to be built from scratch and finished in Tucson. The delivery marked the 1,147th airplane delivered since the company's original Model 23 went to the first customer in 1964.

Gates Learjet announced record international deliveries of 40 new aircraft, valued at more than $100 million, during calendar year 1980. The total represented a 33-percent increase over the previous company export record set in 1975, when 34 airplanes had been delivered abroad. The model most responsible for the global market increase was the newly introduced turbofan-powered Model 35A, which accounted for 31 of the 40 deliveries.

In addition to delivering a record number of airplanes, the company concentrated on safety concerns. In recognition of Gates Learjet's "Checklist '81" series of safety seminars, the FAA presented Harry Combs its Distinguished Service Award on October 16, 1981. The seminar program, endorsed by the FAA, was recognized as the first of its kind in the industry.

Keeping up the momentum of the good news, the first two-for-one stock split in the company's history was announced by Gates Learjet on November 18, 1981. The company had previously issued five 10 percent stock dividends, the first being distributed in March of 1976. Employment at the Tucson facility reached a peak of 2,843 in December. Total company-wide employment at the time was over 7,000 people.

The delivery of 138 new business aircraft during 1981 set a calendar year record for Gates Learjet Corporation. The 138 deliveries exceeded by 18 the previous 120 deliveries logged in 1980. The company achieved its 17th consecutive year of leadership in cumulative business jet deliveries. Learjet airplanes now accounted for 25 percent of the world's total business jet fleet. Since the first delivery in 1964, more than 1,220 Learjets had entered service around the world.

On May 11, 1982, Charlie Gates announced that Combs was elected vice chairman of Gates Learjet Corporation. Having been president since 1971, Combs had led the company during its "dramatic economic turnaround when Gates Learjet increased its sales more than eight times and earnings increased to a level more than six times that which existed when he became president," according to a company news release. Relieving Combs of day-to-day operating responsibilities was Bermar S. "Bib" Stillwell, former chief marketing executive for the company, who was elected president of Gates Learjet. Soon after, he was also elected to the company's board of directors. A week after these executive appointments were made, Gates Learjet added five new service facilities to its growing international product support network. The announcement brought the total number of official service facilities to 27. The new international service facilities were in Stockholm, Sweden; Caracas, Venezuela; Johannesburg, South Africa; Helsinki, Finland; and Bahrain.

In June of 1982 Combs Gates, Inc., Gates Learjet's sales and service subsidiary, purchased Air-Kaman at Bradley International Airport, Windsor Locks, Connecticut. The purchase marked Combs Gates first expansion into the northeast U.S. The new facilities joined a network of five established Combs Gates fixed base operations in Denver, Indianapolis, Palm Springs, Fort Lauderdale, and Arapahoe County, Colorado.

When the general aviation marketplace started a decline in early 1982, employment levels at all Gates Learjet operations, except the Combs Gates subsidiary, also started downward. The general aviation sales slump underway, Charlie Gates had once again decided to put Gates Learjet on the block and devote full attention to Gates' automotive belt and hose business. Adverse economic conditions and stiff foreign competition had cut into Learjet sales and profits, these factors helping Gates to make the decision to sell. The Gates Corporation, which owned 64.8 percent of Gates Learjet Corporation's stock (the rest was owned by the general public), made it clear that it wanted out of the aircraft manufacturing business. After several tentative sales agreements fell through for various reasons, the company's image suffered severely in the marketplace. Customers did not want to buy an airplane and run the risk of owning an orphan if the company failed. It was a difficult time for Gates Learjet sales representatives, who were forced to spend the first 30 minutes of every sales call convincing a prospect that the company was going to survive. Recognizing that it needed to bolster this negative image, in July of 1983 Combs Gates, Inc. opened a newly completed, 44,000-square-foot complex in its Combs Gates Florida base at the Fort Lauderdale/Hollywood International Airport.

On June 25, 1984, Jet Electronics and Technology, Inc., still a Gates Learjet wholly owned subsidiary, was awarded a $3,621,600 order from the U.S. Air Force for self-contained cockpit attitude indicators. The order, one of the largest ever received by the company, bolstered the subsidiary's reputation as a major flight instrument supplier to the military. The 900 units were to be used in F-5, F-111, F-15, and F-16 fighter aircraft. With the company prospering, it was ripe to be sold by Gates Learjet. Operating J.E.T. didn't fit in with the strategic corporate plan of concentrating on aircraft manufacturing. Therefore, on December 23, 1986, BFGoodrich Company acquired J.E.T. for an undisclosed price. Gates Learjet would, however, continue to buy instruments and avionic devices from the firm for its own airplanes.

Diversifying into Aerospace

Seeking to stabilize the company's finances against a recession that would undoubtedly slow down business jet purchases, Gates Learjet announced the formation of a high technology Aerospace Division on July 11, 1984. The new division, based in the company's Wichita manufacturing facilities, was to "provide subcontracting support for the nation's prime contractors in the expanding U.S. defense and space industries." Contracts were already in hand for production of tooling for the forward section of the Rockwell International B-1B bomber, production of the Tomahawk cruise missile tailcone for General Dynamics, remanufacture of KC-135 engine nacelles for Boeing, and machining of missile carrier components for Southwest Truck.

The relatively young Aerospace Division was selected by Martin Marietta Corporation in September of 1985 to build intertank panels and a support beam for the Space Shuttle's main booster rockets. The $14 million contract was the company's first entry in the space program. During the fall of 1986, more than 100 employees were added to the division's workforce as a result of new aerospace contracts, including an agreement to supply tooling services to the Boeing Military Airplane Company through 1987. Approximately $6,000,000 was committed for new specialized equipment in the division. A skin milling machine, automatic riveter, automated processing line, robotic painting system, hot form machine, and roll form machine were installed to expand the division's capability in aerospace subcontracting.

The Aerospace Division continued to make a significant inroad into aerospace contracting and subcontracting by early 1987. The division added still another 150 employees to its workforce upon winning $3,500,000 in contracts during the first 45 days of the year. These contracts included tooling services for Boeing Military Airplane Company, F-16 tooling services for General Dynamics' Fort Worth Division, assembly tooling work for Martin Marietta's Space Shuttle external tank program, C-130 fuel tanks and cradle assemblies for the U.S. Air Force, and Maverick missile work for the Hughes Aircraft Company. For the first time in its history, in the spring of 1987 Gates Learjet was named one of America's top 100 defense contractors. The company ranked 78th on the government's list of prime contract awards for fiscal year 1986 based on a sales volume of $232,595,000. Boosting the contract award figure upward was an Air Force buy of 80 C-21A airplanes, the military equivalent of the Model 35A, a fleet which had previously been leased. Other major contributors were the continuing contractor C-21A logistic support provided by Gates Learjet Aircraft Services Corporation (GLASCO) and Jet Electronics & Technology (before it was sold to BFGoodrich).

On September 25, 1987, the Aerospace Division delivered the first Space Shuttle parts to the Martin Marietta Corporation. The parts consisted of the external tank panels for the spacecraft's highly sophisticated propulsion system. The $14 million contract called for 20 shipsets to be delivered over the following three years.

Nineteen eighty-four saw Gates Learjet celebrate the 20th anniversary of the first production delivery of a Learjet. The third Model 23 to be built had entered service with the Chemical and Industrial Corporation of Cincinnati, Ohio, on October 13, 1964. It carried the FAA registration number N200Y. Combs Gates also opened a new $4 million airport complex at Windsor Locks, Connecticut, in 1984. Facilities included a 4,000-square-foot executive terminal, a 23,000-square-foot service hangar, and an additional 10,000 square feet for engine, electrical, hydraulic, and avionics repair. All six Combs Gates bases continued to be ranked by pilots in the top one percent of more than 5,000 fixed base operations.

On February 21, 1986, the corporate headquarters was officially relocated to Tucson from Wichita. At the time, the company's emphasis had shifted to the desert city, and it was logical to move all remaining corporate functions there.

A major modification and custom completion center was established by Gates Learjet as an expansion of the company's Tucson and Wichita customer service facilities, in January of 1987. To increase revenues, the company would now perform modification work on not only Learjets, but other aircraft as well. Total capabilities were offered: refurbishment with customized paint, interiors, and avionics. New airplanes coming off the Wichita assembly line were still being flown "green" to Tucson and customized to a customer's specific desires.

James B. Taylor, long a prominent figure in corporate aviation, was elected vice chairman of the board of directors and chief executive officer of Gates Learjet Corporation on April 16, 1985. The former World War II Navy fighter pilot's career included stints as vice president and general manager of Cessna Aircraft's commercial jet marketing division, and more recently, chairman of Canadair, Inc., builder of the Challenger business jet. Combs, the former vice chairman, had at last decided to retire to his sprawling Colorado ranch. That was, of course, exactly what he had planned to do before getting involved with Gates Learjet after Charlie Gates bought the company in 1967. On June 17, 1985, Taylor was elected president and chief executive officer of Gates Learjet, following the resignation of Bib Stillwell. As the man who successfully introduced the Falcon, Citation, and Challenger business jets to the world, his qualifications for the job were indisputable. With Combs and Stillwell gone, running the company would tax his abilities to the fullest. Ironically, under Taylor's direction, the Citation was a direct competitor of the Learjet.

On December 4, 1985, Harry Combs, still a member of the Gates Learjet Corporation board, was awarded the Wright Brothers Memorial Trophy for 1985. Administered by the National Aeronautic Association, the trophy symbolized a lifetime contribution to aviation. It was presented at the Aero Club of Washington's annual dinner by then Vice President George Bush.

A New Owner Takes Over

On August 5, 1987, Gates Corporation announced a definitive agreement to sell its 64.8 percent interest in Gates Learjet to Integrated Acquisition, Inc., a wholly owned subsidiary of Integrated Resources, Inc. The agreement called for Gates to sell its 7,840,585 Learjet shares for $7.25 each, or $56,844,241. A principal activity of Integrated Acquisition was to engage in the acquisition of established operating companies through leveraged buyouts. The parent company, which has its headquarters in New York City, has been described as a leading financial services firm. It is engaged in the sale of life insurance, investment counseling for private accounts, and mutual funds. It is also involved in the organization, management, and sale of public and private limited partnerships.

Integrated Acquisition, Inc. completed the purchase of the Gates Corporation's 64.8-percent interest in Gates Learjet on September 9, 1987. Integrated immediately announced that it planned to make a tender offer for the remaining 4.3 million shares of Gates Learjet stock held by the public. Not long afterward, Integrated acquired the balance of these shares through the tender offer, giving Integrated 96.1 percent of the total shares outstanding. At that point, Gates Learjet Corporation was taken private and its stock delisted on the American Stock Exchange.

In early September, Integrated announced a restructuring of the Learjet board of directors. Jim Taylor, president and chief executive officer, was named chairman of the board. Other board members were Robert J. Edgreen, president of Integrated Acquisition; William T. Warburton, executive vice president of Integrated Acquisition; Murray Forman, vice president of Integrated Acquisition; and William L. Adair, senior executive vice president of Integrated Resources. William A. Boettger, Gates Learjet vice president and general manager of the Aircraft Division (and a 22-year Cessna veteran), was named president of that division.

Integrated Acquisition announced on October 23, 1987, that it had acquired 96.1 percent of the shares of Gates Learjet common stock. On October 30, 1987, Integrated announced that it had consummated the acquisition of Gates Learjet Corporation. No sooner had the industry gained wind of the Learjet acquisition, speculation abounded that the acquiring company was looking for nothing more than an opportunity to buy Gates Learjet at a bargain price with the intent to later unload it for much more. To dispel such rumors, Integrated announced that, although it would consolidate the company to cut costs in the short term, it would also invest the capital necessary to make the company's products highly competitive in the worldwide business jet market.

Beverly N. (Bev) Lancaster was appointed vice president and general manager of the company's Aerospace Division on November 16th. Lancaster was a 29-year Boeing veteran before retiring from that company in July 1986. At Learjet, he was made responsible for all operations in the Division, the high technology manufacturing unit organized by Gates Learjet in 1984 in an attempt to capture more aerospace industry contracts. The aerospace business could be used to bolster the company's finances, compensating for the seesaw curves typifying business jet sales activity. A month later, Boettger and Lancaster were elected to the corporation's board of directors.

January 21, 1988 saw Lancaster named president and chief executive officer, succeeding Taylor, who resigned to pursue other business interests. During his tenure, Taylor had eliminated the company's debt, dropped unprofitable projects, expanded international sales, and spearheaded final development of the Model 31 and 55 Learjets. Later in January, Boettger was named executive vice president of Gates Learjet Corporation.

Bev Lancaster, chairman and chief executive officer of Learjet Corporation. Learjet Corp.

On March 23, 1988, the company's board of directors elected Anthony M. Hain, Gates Learjet's longtime treasurer and chief financial officer, to the Gates Learjet board of directors. A month later, the board decided to change the company's name from Gates Learjet Corporation to Learjet Corporation. The airplane itself was now to be called, quite simply, the "Learjet." The same month, AMR Services Corp. signed an agreement with Integrated Acquisition to acquire Combs Gates Denver, a corporate affiliate of Learjet with six aviation service centers. AMR Services is the aviation services subsidiary of AMR Corporation, the parent company of American Airlines. On June 30, 1988, AMR completed the acquisition of Combs Gates, soon changing the aircraft service network's name to AMR Combs. In the FBO business, AMR had already realized the value of identifying with Combs, long a recognized entity in aviation sales and service.

Learjet Corporation announced that Brian E. Barents was appointed president of the company on March 1, 1989. Lancaster was elevated to chairman of the board and chief executive officer, succeeding Edgreen, who resigned from Integrated. Earlier in the decade, as an executive with Cessna, Barents had been heavily involved with the marketing of that company's entire product line.

Brian E. Barents, president of Learjet Corporation. Learjet Corp.

Following its acquisition of the company, Integrated indicated that it had taken steps to restructure the company to operate profitably at its current production rates. Early 1988 saw the company make a detailed study of the manufacturing and completion work being done in Tucson with the aim of possibly consolidating the work at the company's Wichita location. In February 1988 a decision was made to move Learjet manufacturing operations and corporate headquarters back to Wichita. The move was to be accomplished gradually throughout the year and completed by year end. Stretching the move over several months ensured that the planned Learjet production schedule would not be impacted. According to the company, the move would result in appreciable cost savings by eliminating redundancies in inventory and management and by eliminating transportation costs between the two locations.

The vacated space in Tucson amounted to approximately 322,500 square feet, which was intended to be sold to another aviation related activity. The operations continuing in Tucson today include customer service, resale marketing, aircraft modification, and sales.

Learjet Corporation's sprawling Wichita plant and headquarters, situated adjacent to that city's municipal airport. Learjet Corp.

An Exciting Past and Promising Future

For the first time since 1983, during 1988 Learjet Corporation turned a profit. The company delivered 23 airplanes with total sales pegged at $218,450,000. Through 1988, Learjet corporation had built nearly 1,600 airplanes for the domestic, international, and military markets. These aircraft had been sold in 37 different countries. The largest fleet of Learjets was located in the U.S., accounting for well over 1,000 airplanes. Flight International of Atlanta was the largest single commercial Learjet operator in the world, having over 50 of the airplanes in its fleet. The second largest concentration was in Brazil with over 80 ships, followed by Mexico with 45 and West Germany and Canada with 26 and 23 aircraft respectively. Over 430 had been delivered overseas since the first export delivery occurred in 1965.

Three vastly different kinds of owners and 25 years of turmoil characterize the Learjet story. In the serenity of its middle years, the Learjet Corporation has mellowed, enjoying an air of stability at last. Never a humdrum airplane, or company for that matter, Bill Lear had set the stage for the future when he said ''let's do something different!'' The Learjet certainly turned out to be very different.

3
The Model 20 Series Creates a Revolution

Once described as "the only airplane that looks like it's going 600 miles an hour sitting on the ground," the Lear Jet Model 23 made its debut at the world's airports during the final months of 1964. Then, as now, it attracted stares wherever it landed. It soon established a reputation as a speedster—a hot rod among corporate jets. In pilot circles, the word also got around that it was a plane that took a tender touch to fly. It was said that if a pilot let a problem get too far out of hand, it could easily be too late to correct it. Most new Lear Jet captains graduated from Convairs, DC-3s, and Lodestars—the typical corporate "barges" of the 1950s. Few of them had previous jet experience, yet most of them managed their transition to the Model 23 without major problems. Most airline captains had succeeded in transitioning from propeller to jet transports and corporate pilots were showing that they were no different.

Wherever the sexy jet would land, a crowd would gather. It became an instant celebrity—and a celebrity's jet. Among the celebrity users were Frank Sinatra, Johnny Carson, Danny Kaye, Richard Nixon, Steve Lawrence and Eydie Gorme, Joe E. Brown, Madame Chiang Kai-shek, singer Roger Miller, Art Linkletter, the Smothers Brothers, Bob Cummings, and newsmen Howard K. Smith and Peter Jennings.

The Lear Jet's compact size was a direct result of the original design philosophy. Bill Lear wanted to offer high performance at a relatively low cost. Hence, the airframe was small. The slick design prompted competitors to publicly question the comfort and practicality of the aircraft. The somewhat cramped access to cabin seating proved to be a brief inconvenience; once seated, passengers were comfortable. Crew seating was especially comfortable. The lack of a door between the cockpit and cabin wasn't found to be a problem either. The informality was pleasant, as passengers could watch crew activities on the flight deck. Cockpit room was at a premium—a requirement to accommodate the sleek exterior fuselage contours. Bill Lear's response to prospects who complained about its cabin size was: "Hell, you don't stand up in your Cadillac, do you?"

Smugly dubbed a "motorcycle jet" by a manufacturer of a larger corporate jet, the Model 23 had no restroom facilities. Lear felt that offering such an amenity was an admission that an airplane was taking too long to get to its destination. As the airplane's range increased incrementally over the years, that initial logic was abandoned.

Swift as a Bird Yet Built Like a Tank

Outside, the Model 23 looked sleek, rakish, and advanced: but Lear wasn't about to take technical risks inside with its airframe structure and systems. Conventional semi-monocoque, light sheet metal alloy construction was used for the fuselage, wing and empennage sections. Likewise, to reduce risk, only proven technologies were used in the design of the electrical, electronics, hydraulic, pressurization, instrument, flight control, and powerplant systems. Lear manufactured 85 percent of the airplane within the walls of his Wichita factory, unusual in the aircraft industry, to maintain close surveillance on quality. It was also the most economical way to approach the matter, avoiding the built-in profits that subcontractors would have charged.

To gain entry to the airplane's cockpit and cabin, the Model 23 uses a split, outwardly extending clamshell-type door on the left forward side of the cabin. By contrast, most commercial jetliners used a "plug" type door, which closes from the inside out. Despite early skepticism that the Lear-designed door might fail in flight, years of service experience proved that it worked reliably. It's efficient from a space and weight standpoint because it doesn't consume valuable cabin space and, becoming an integral part of the fuselage, carries airframe structural loads when closed. The door also serves as a boarding step—steps are built into the lower door section to help the crew and passengers board the aircraft. Ten large steel pins secure the vault-type door to the fuselage when the door is in the closed position, making it an integral part of the cabin structure when the cabin is pressurized.

The Model 23's airframe structure is designed to be rugged and damage-tolerant, exceeding the structural certification requirements for commercial jetliners. During certification, the fuselage underwent 50,000 pressurization cycles to ensure that the entry door and the rest of the fuselage structure would not fail in flight after enduring years of take-offs and landings. The fuselage structure is built up around a main keel beam running the length of the cabin. Tying into the keel beam, the fuselage frames are shaped in the natural round shape of a pressurized vessel. Relatively small fuselage skin panels assure low stress levels and long airframe life. Both the aircraft's wing and tail assemblies feature multiple spar construction. The wing itself has eight spars, earning the airplane the distinction of being one of the sturdiest airplanes ever built. Proof of this rugged construction is the wing skin: it's nearly one-fourth inch thick at its inboard end. The vertical and horizontal tail surfaces feature five-spar construction. Whether wing, empennage, or fuselage, the single failure of a structural member, such as a spar, will not cause a catastrophic failure since a nearby member can absorb the additional load.

The wing is attached to the fuselage at eight points, facilitating removal for "demate" inspections. Engine cowlings are quickly removable for maintenance access. Further aiding maintainability, all major Model 23 electrical and hydraulic system components are grouped together and easily accessible by opening a fuselage access panel aft of the wing.

The Model 23's windshield became Bill Lear's pride and joy. It is divided into two sections, each built up from three laminated layers of stretched acrylic plastic. More than an inch thick, the windshield maintains its strength over the wide temperature range the airplane is exposed to during flight operations. For certification purposes, it was tested to withstand the impact of a four-pound object fired at 345 miles per hour. The material is so strong, it can't be cracked with an axe. To dramatize its strength, Bill Lear kept a section of the windshield on his office floor to demonstrate its strength to visitors by jumping up and down on it. A high-capacity defogging system keeps the inside surface clear under the most extreme conditions. On the outside, a hot bleed-air powered system keeps the windshield clear, obviating the need for unreliable mechanical windshield wipers.

Rugged Landing Gear

The Model 23, along with all other Learjet models, features a tricycle, fully retractable landing gear. Dual wheel main landing gear assemblies are fully retractable via hydraulic actuators powered by the airplane's main hydraulic system. Each main wheel assembly (which incorporates disk brakes and anti-skid braking control) is stowed in wheel wells under the wing center section. The forward-retracting single nosewheel assembly features a "chine" type of tire to disperse water sideways away from engine compressor inlets during operation on wet runways. Nosewheel steering is accomplished via an electrical actuator, controlled by buttons on the pilot and copilot control wheels.

A single lever lock switch on the instrument panel is used to electrically activate the hydraulic landing gear actuators. Each landing gear leg is maintained in the extended position by an integral lock in the actuating cylinder. The inboard main gear doors close after gear extension. Hydro-mechanical uplocks are provided for each door. Loss of hydraulic system pressure will not cause disengagement of the uplocks or downlocks, making the landing gear system fail-safe. Should the airplane suffer complete hydraulic system failure, a high-pressure pneumatic backup system, operating at 1,800 to 3,000 psi, serves to extend the landing gear and operate the brakes.

High capacity, multiple disc power brakes are activated by valves controlled by toe brakes above each pilot's rudder pedals. A fully modulated anti-skid system is installed on each of the four main gear wheels. The anti-skid system, manufactured by the Hydro-Aire Division of Crane, Inc., provides maximum braking effectiveness on any surface, whether wet, dry, or covered with ice or snow. It also provides automatic brake snubbing during gear retraction. The system consists of a small tachometer generator mounted adjacent to each main gear wheel, a computer module, and hydraulic solenoid valves. The computer monitors the rotational speed of each braked wheel (as sensed by the generators), alternately activating and releasing the brake for each wheel whenever the rate of deceleration of a rotating wheel exceeds acceptable values, signifying a skid condition. Four small anti-skid annunciator lights are mounted atop the pilot's instrument panel. Each is connected to a corresponding anti-skid generator in a braked wheel. The lights monitor each channel of the system, and are illuminated if the system malfunctions.

Simple Flight Controls

Primary flight controls, including ailerons, elevators, and rudder are controlled manually via a system of conventional mechanical control cables, bellcranks, and pulleys. To enhance aileron aerodynamic effectiveness, vortex generators are installed on both the top and bottom surfaces of the outboard wing on each side of the airplane. Hydraulic boost is not required. Likewise, trim tab control is conventional. An electromechanical screw jack positions the movable horizontal stabilizer in response to actuating rocker-type switches on the pilot and copilot control wheels. The same switches control an actuator for varying the position of the aileron trim tab. Rudder trim is provided via an electrome-chanical actuator located in the empennage area and controlled by a rudder trim switch located on the lower center cockpit pedestal. An adjacent flap switch, aided by a panel-mounted flap position indicator, is used to incrementally control accurate positioning of the wing flaps. The flaps are actuated by a hydraulic cylinder located adjacent to each flap surface. A mechanical interconnect between the two surfaces prevents any possibility of asymmetric flap extension.

Aerodynamic spoilers are located on the upper wing surfaces, forward of the wing flaps. A switch on the control pedestal extends the spoilers by activating a solenoid valve controlling a hydraulic cylinder on each side of the wing. To benefit from fuel-conserving high altitudes, most jets maintain a relatively high altitude until just before landing. A steep letdown profile is then used for descending into the airport area. By deploying the wing spoilers at altitude, a pilot can rapidly achieve such a descent. Immediately after touchdown, spoilers are again used to destroy lift, transferring wing loads onto the landing gear to improve braking effectiveness and shorten landing rollouts.

Stall Detection and Prevention

With its thin, high-speed wing, the Model 23 quickly established a reputation for being a "hot" airplane during approach and landing phases. Because there was always fear about the possibility of the airplane entering an unrecoverable "deep" stall, the FAA required that the aircraft be equipped with both a stick shaker and pusher. When the Model 23 was in slow flight at a high angle of attack, its stall behavior was said to be largely unpredictable. The airplane could roll off in one direction or the other. Worse yet, wake created by the wing and engine nacelles at high angles of attack could blank out the T-tail, causing the airplane to enter an unrecoverable stall. Sinking to the ground in a steep nose-up attitude, there would be no hope for the crew in such a situation. With this in mind, the FAA mandated that the airplane never actually be stalled. Instead, effective stall warning and stick pusher systems were provided to keep crews vigilant regarding a possible stall. Connected into the elevator's flight control system, the "stick shaker" vibrates the control column as the airplane approaches a stall (before the pusher takes effect), to warn the pilot of the impending stall. If the stalling condition is allowed to progress further, the "pusher" forces the control column forward, lowering the angle of attack, to prevent an actual stall from occurring. The stall shaker and pusher systems are activated by small, electrically heated stall sensing vanes located on the airplane's forward fuselage. The sensing system electronics are duplicated to provide fail-safe stall warning indications.

Reliable Hydraulic System

The Model 23's landing gear, inboard landing gear doors, flaps, spoilers, and wheel brakes are powered by a 1,500-pound-per-square-inch (psi) hydraulic system. Two vari-able-volume, constant-pressure pumps, driven by the accessory gearbox of each engine, supply the necessary pressure. Either pump is capable of supplying enough pressure maintaining the 1,500 psi system requirement. Design features minimized pressure spikes to enhance reliability and provide increased capacity for cold weather landing gear retrac-tion. Further protection is provided by thermal relief valves and micronic filters located in both the system's pressure and return lines. Hydraulic fluid level may be visually checked by the crew during preflight inspections via a sight gauge on the system's reservoir. A cockpit gauge indicates hydraulic pressure and a low-pressure warning light annunciates system failure.

Either engine-driven hydraulic pump can operate the entire airplane hydraulic system. An auxiliary electrically-driven pump can operate the system if both engine-driven pumps fail. The auxiliary pump is automatically energized by a pressure switch whenever system pressure drops below 1,200 psi.

Electrically-driven firewall shutoff valves are located adjacent to each engine firewall. They are used to shut off the flow of hydraulic fluid to the nacelle in the event of a fire. Within the nacelle itself, corrosion-resistant steel lines and fire-resistant hoses provide additional protection against fire or physical damage.

The Fuel System Is Simple, Too

Mindful of the fact that fuel system failure and pilot fuel mismanagement had often resulted in business aircraft accidents, Lear designed the Model 23's fuel system for maximum reliability and simplicity. Each engine has a totally independent fuel system. The Model 23's fuel is stored in tip tanks, tanks within the wing, and in a fuselage bladder fuel cell. The reinforced fuselage fuel compartment, lined with a Uniroyal rubber bladder, is located immediately forward of the engine mounting beams.

The left wing and left tip tanks feed the left engine during normal operation, with the right wing and tip tanks feeding the right engine. Fuel in the fuselage tank can be moved via a transfer pump to either wing tank. A crossflow valve equalizes the fuel levels in both wing tanks, allowing all the onboard fuel to be transferred to either engine. The wing tanks and tip tanks incorporate baffles to prevent sloshing and fuel shifting during extreme flight attitudes. The wing tip and fuselage tanks can gravity-feed about half their fuel capacity into the main wing tanks in the event of a transfer pump malfunction.

A dc motor-powered fuel pump is used for engine starting and as backup for the tip tank-mounted jet pumps, which replaced the Model 23's complicated electrically driven pumps. The jet pumps provide the pressure required to supply fuel to the engines. Once the engines are started, the electric pump is switched off and the jet pumps take over. The jet pumps are operated by bypassing high pressure motive fuel from the engine-driven fuel pumps through the jet pumps. Bypassed motive fuel is directed through a venturi into a larger line. The low pressure area created within the venturi picks up additional fuel and carries it, via the main fuel line, back to the engine on each side. The nonelectrical, "ejector-type" jet pumps have no moving parts, offering operators maximum reliability. If a jet pump should ever fail, the standby motor-driven pumps supply fuel to both engines. Each dc-powered standby pump has sufficient capacity to meet the engine's requirements at all altitudes and flight attitudes. A fuel vent system maintains a positive internal pressure differential in all tanks. The venting allows all tanks to remain within limits during maximum rates of climb or descent. Assuming a worst case failure scenario, the engine-driven fuel pumps are capable of supplying fuel to the engines below 25,000 feet if both the jet pumps and backup electrically-driven pumps fail.

Fuel system cockpit instrumentation includes dual fuel flowmeters, reading in pounds per hour, and a fuel quantity indicator, reading in pounds. The quantity indicator has an associated selector switch for displaying the fuel level in the tank selected by the switch. Warning lights for low fuel pressure and low quantity are provided. Control of the various airframe fuel pumps is via toggle switches, with associated annunciator lights indicating pump operating status.

The Right Engine Makes It All Possible

The Models 23, 24, 25, along with their much later Model 28 and 29 variants, are powered by various versions of the General Electric CJ610 turbojet engine, a derivative of GE's J85 family of jet engines. The CJ610 is an axial flow engine utilizing the same gas generator and many of the accessory components of the military J85 and commercial CF700 turbofan engines. The latter powers the Falcon 20 and Sabreliner 75 business jets. The J85 has been in production for both military and commercial applications since 1958. Over 15,000 engines have been produced, logging over 35 million flight hours.

All CJ610 and J85 engines feature a single rotor (also known as a single spool) construction, using two turbine stages, three main bearings, and a straight-through airflow design. Simple in aerodynamic design, no reverse or radial flow patterns complicate its operation. The CJ610 features a compressor and turbine casing that is horizontally split for easy inspection and maintenance access. A complete hot section inspection can be performed with the engine installed on the airplane. The engine's stator vanes and inlet guide vanes can also be replaced without removing the engine from the ship. Aiding maintainability, replacement of turbine wheels, diaphragms, and combustor can be accomplished

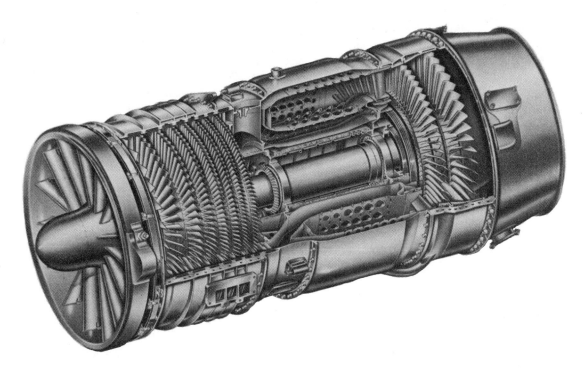

Cutaway view of General Electric CJ610 turbojet engine used to power Models 23, 24, 25, 28, and 29.
General Electric Co.

without completely disassembling the engine. In addition, all fuel nozzles and ignitors can be individually replaced. The first stage compressor blades can be replaced without disassembly or removal of the rotor from the engine. In the engine's hot section, the turbine buckets can be replaced without rebalancing the rotating turbine assembly.

Thrust characteristics of the CJ610 are perfectly matched to the high performance requirements of the Learjet—performance which provides significant improvements over competitive small turboprop and turbofan airplanes. A high engine thrust-to-weight ratio and lower turbojet thrust lapse rate translates into shorter balanced field length, higher rate of climb, and good payloads, especially from high altitude airports on hot days. At higher altitudes the lower thrust lapse rate means a higher cruise thrust is available. This allows for an optimum aircraft lift/drag ratio, extended range, and higher cruise speeds and altitudes.

On all GE-powered Learjets, a power lever for each engine is mounted between the pilots on a center pedestal. Engine start, ignition, and fuel management switches and related annunciator lights are located in the lower instrument panel area and a console extending rearward from the pedestal. Round dial engine instruments are grouped in the center instrument panel area.

In 1958, the J85 was introduced into military service with the Northrop T-38A Talon jet trainer, and later the derivative F-5A Freedom Fighter series airplanes. In 1961, the first civil variant of the J85, the CJ610-1, was certificated by the FAA. This milestone was followed in 1964 with certification of the CJ610-4, which featured a four percent reduction in engine weight. That same year, the CJ610-1 first became operational on a civil aircraft aboard the Model 23. In 1966, the Model 24 was certified with the CJ610-4. Also that year, the CJ610-6 obtained FAA approval. This improved version featured a 3.5-percent thrust increase with a two-percent cruise specific fuel consumption (SFC) reduction. In 1967, the Model 25 was certified with the CJ610-6. In 1968, the Model 24B was also certified with this engine. The Models 24C and 24D, 25B, and 25C received certification using the CJ610-6 in 1970. The CJ610-8A is the latest model in the long series of CJ610 powerplants. This engine, with improved maximum altitude capability and cruise thrust, is standard equipment in the latest 20 Series airplanes. In addition to application on the Learjet, CJ610 engines power the Commodore Jet, Hansa Jet, and Israel Aircraft Industries (IAI) Westwind.

General Electric points out that the owner of a GE-powered Learjet 20 Series airplane can fly for 10 years—at the rate of 500 hours per year—without needing a scheduled overhaul. This also means that if a Learjet owner decides to trade in the airplane, at six years for example, the new owner obtains a used airplane with 2,000 hours of engine time-between-overhaul (TBO) remaining, which translates into four more years of use. The CJ610-8A, featuring a 5,000 hour TBO, represents more than a six-fold increase from the first CJ610s that powered early Model 23s. When the engine first went into service on the Model 23, it was only approved for an 800 hour TBO.

Electrical Power System

The Model 23, in common with later models, uses a direct current electrical power supply system. Primary power is 28 volts dc, with a secondary ac power supply system supplying 115 volts ac. Most of the airplane's devices and systems are energized by dc power.

Two 400 ampere, 28-volt dc engine starter-generators, driven by the accessory gearbox of each engine, supply the primary dc power. During engine starting, the starter-generators function as starter motors to crank the engines. Starts can be accomplished either on internal battery power or via 28-volt dc external ground power. A standard ground power receptacle, which is located aft of the wing on the fuselage, serves to connect external power to the airplane for engine starting, operating ground air conditioning, or performing routine system checkouts on the ground.

Following engine lightoff, and when de-energized as a starter, each starter-generator reverts to dc generator operation. Either generator has sufficient capacity to supply all of the airplane's electrical loads. Two 22-ampere-hour nickel-cadmium (ni-cad) batteries supply power for engine starting and emergency power in the event of total generator failure. Later 20 Series models substituted lead-acid batteries for the ni-cad units, due to problems common to ni-cad batteries. Two solid-state inverters, each capable of supplying 1 kVA of power, supply 115 volts ac for the Model 23's instruments and avionics. Either inverter can power any or all of the equipment normally powered by the ac power distribution system.

The dc power distribution system consists of three buses: pilot's main bus, co-pilot's main bus, and essential dc bus. The left generator normally supplies the pilot's main bus, and the right generator supplies the co-pilot's bus. A bus tie breaker connecting the two buses is open during normal system operation, allowing the dc generators to operate independently of each other, delivering power to their respective loads. Should one of the generators drop off-line, due to engine failure or system malfunction, the bus tie breaker automatically closes, connecting the two main buses together and instantly powering all dc loads off the remaining operative generator.

The two aircraft batteries are connected to a main battery bus, which in turn connects to right and left essential dc buses. Both essential buses are normally connected together via a bus tie breaker. Should a circuit malfunction occur in either bus, the breaker opens, isolating the malfunctioning or failed bus from the "healthy" one.

The two solid-state inverters used to supply ac power are designated as primary and secondary inverters. The primary unit is powered off the left generator bus, with the secondary unit powered off the right generator bus. During normal operation, both inverters operate in parallel. A control box regulates the outputs from each inverter, maintaining synchronized voltage and phase. If a fault occurs in one of the inverters or its distribution circuits, that inverter is isolated automatically from the rest of the ac system. An interconnecting bus tie breaker between the two buses opens, and the two buses then operate independently of each other. Typical loads operated from the ac buses include radio communications and navigation equipment, gyro systems, autopilot, brake anti-skid system, and certain engine instruments.

During the 1950s, Bill Lear had experienced total electrical system failure in his Learstar, while flying over the Rockies at night during a storm. The cause of that incident happened to be pilot error but he wanted no repeat of such a terrifying experience with his new jet. Powering the pilot's and copilot's critical instrument systems from different buses achieved the redundancy and safety that he mandated for the new business jet.

A number of safety provisions are incorporated to ensure continued electrical system operation in the event of an in-flight emergency. Either dc generator or either ac inverter can supply all of its respective loads in the event its companion generator or inverter fails.

The dc and ac circuits and buses are physically separated throughout the fuselage to prevent total primary power failure if a wiring bundle should be damaged from an in-flight fire or explosion. The dc and ac systems both operate in parallel fashion, evenly distributing the loads between components to minimize component stress and achieve maximum service life.

As he had back in the Learstar days, Bill Lear wanted no distracting overhead switch or instrument panels, which he felt could cause possible vertigo. Lear had strong personal likes and dislikes about cockpits, wanting every switch, control, and instrument within his normal forward field of view. Complying with this dictate, his cockpit designers placed all electrical switches on the main instrument panel and circuit breakers on auxiliary panels alongside the pilot and co-pilot seats. The all-important bus tie breakers are located on the co-pilot's circuit breaker panel. To monitor electrical system health, cockpit instrumentation includes dc and ac system voltmeters and dc ammeters, along with power failure warning lights.

Exterior lighting consists of landing lights located on each main landing gear strut. Dual electromechanical rotating beacons for anticollision warning are provided, one atop the vertical stabilizer and one beneath the fuselage on its centerline below the wing. Conventional wingtip and tail position lights, along with high-intensity strobe lighting that became available later, are provided for additional anticollision warning.

A Comfortable Cabin Environment

In its day, the Learstar had ushered in a new era in cabin luxury and speed for executive transports, but it possessed one nagging flaw: it wasn't pressurized. Recalling how he was forced to reach for an oxygen mask at altitude, Lear was also intent on providing the best pressurization and air conditioning system for the Model 23.

Cabin pressurization is achieved using conditioned engine bleed air, that enters the cabin through air distribution ducts located along the floor spanning both sides of the cabin. Control of the pressurization system is via a pneumatic pressure control system. Controls are located on the instrument panel forward of the co-pilot. They can be adjusted to vary cabin altitude, cabin rate of climb (or descent), and maximum pressure differential setting. Separate instruments, adjacent to the controls, indicate cabin altitude and rate of climb. A maximum cabin pressure differential of 9.4 psi provides an 8,000-foot cabin while flying at cruise altitude. Although the system is controlled automatically, the crew can override the system at any time, manually adjusting the pressurization system to suit prevailing preferences.

If the automatic control system fails, the pressurization can be controlled manually. The system features a pneumatic safety valve to prevent any possibility of over-pressurization. Explosive cabin decompression is not likely due to the fail-safe design of the fuselage structure. If it's necessary to use an alternate method to pressurize the cabin due to the failure of the primary system, the windshield de-fog system can be used. Air output from the de-fog system can provide a cabin altitude not exceeding 15,000 feet while flying at a cruise altitude of 45,000 feet.

Undoubtedly, Lear also recalled the sweltering days in the cockpit of the older airplanes, while awaiting passengers on the ramp or poised at the end of a hot runway waiting for takeoff clearance. He insisted on a high-capacity air conditioning system, operable both in-flight and on the ground. A vapor-cycle cabin air conditioning system was developed, using Freon R-12 as a refrigerant. The system's compressor, powered by a dc motor, is located in the tailcone area together with an accompanying condenser. An evaporator unit, operating in conjunction with a recirculating fan in the cabin, provides maximum cooling effectiveness for both crew and passengers. Being electrically-driven, the air conditioning system is capable of cooling down the cabin on the ground by idling one engine, or prior to main engine start by using an external 28-volt dc auxiliary power unit.

To heat the cockpit and cabin, engine bleed air is used to preheat fresh incoming air passing through a heat exchanger. A ram air duct directs outside air into the exchanger. Cabin ventilation is normally provided by the airplane's pressurization system. The cabin air is changed at a rate of 11 pounds per minute. The entire volume of air in the cabin is changed in about one and one-fourth minutes. If the airplane is flown unpressurized and the cabin pressure is below ram pressure, a ram check valve opens, allowing ram air to pass through the cabin for ventilation.

Ice Protection for Safe Operation

The Model 23's ice protection system assures that the airplane can fly through known icing conditions. Windshield anti-icing is accomplished by directing engine compressor bleed air over the outside surface of the windshield. De-fogging of the windshield's inside surface is achieved by directing a continuous stream of conditioned air across it. The exterior windshield anti-ice system is backed up by a methyl alcohol system. If the normal windshield anti-ice system should malfunction, the methyl alcohol system may be activated to spray the solution on the windshield through nose-mounted anti-ice nozzles. While flying in icing conditions, a motor-driven alcohol pump is used to spray methyl alcohol over the radome from a small nozzle located in the radome itself.

Anti-ice protection for the wing leading edges and engine guide vanes is also provided by engine compressor bleed air. The air tapped off the compressor sections of each engine is routed through a pressure regulator before being piped to the leading edges of the wing. When "anti-ice" is switched on by the pilot, solenoid-controlled valves admit bleed air into the leading edges and engine inlet guide vanes.

On the Model 23, no ice protection was incorporated for the horizontal stabilizer. On later aircraft, however, the leading edge of the horizontal stabilizer, together with the leading edges of the engine nacelles, pitot heads, static air ports, and stall warning vanes, are all electrothermally heated, powered by the airplane's 28-volt dc power supply.

Full Instrumentation and Avionics

The Model 23's crew station features a "dual blind" instrument arrangement, with duplicate primary flight instruments for each pilot. Electromechanical flight directors and horizontal situation indicators are provided, as well as dual radio magnetic indicators (RMIs). The standard T-type of instrument arrangement is used for familiarity and to facilitate fast scanning by pilots. On the early Model 23s, instrument attitude and directional information was supplied by Bill Lear's own vertical gyro and directional gyro systems (Vertisyn and Directisyn) and autopilot. The Lear Jet instruments were World War II-era gyros modified with synchro pickoffs for supplying signals to both the cockpit displays and autopilot.

With Lear in the captain's seat, his wife, Moya Olsen Lear, exits a Model 23 after a night flight and landing on a snowy runway. Moya Olsen Lear collection.

The airline-type systems of the Jet Commander proved to be stiff competition for Lear. Detractors of the Model 23 inferred that the ship was marginal from a safety standpoint, because it did not have the sophisticated airline-style systems typifying the Jet Commander. The Jet Commander featured two dc generators and two ac alternators, along with a sophisticated frequency conversion system, to supply 400 Hz ac power directly from the alternators. Most Jet Commanders also featured Collins FD-108 pictorial flight directors—the state-of-the-art during the 1960s. Many Model 23s initially featured lesser Collins PN-101 navigation displays interfaced with Lear attitude indicators. Because Bill Lear wanted to sell the Model 23 with his own flight instrumentation, few factory avionics options were available from other vendors, making it difficult to please customers who wished to choose from a wide range of avionics.

Bill Lear's major achievements in postwar aviation were in the autopilot area, with the L-5 military autopilot winning him the Collier Trophy. In civil aviation, his L-2 electronic autopilot had set new standards for light general aviation aircraft. The all-transistorized Lear L-102 found its way into the early airline jet transports, proving its capability in 1962 when a French Caravelle jetliner made the world's first "blind" landing in Europe. When it came to the Model 23, Lear made sure the new airplane had the best of everything in autopilot features. It has been said that some customers bought the airplane because of its autopilot. True or not, the autopilot continued the Lear tradition of reliability, simplicity, and capability in autopilot design.

The J.E.T. FC-110 autopilot became the standard Lear Jet autopilot. It stabilizes the airplane in rough flight conditions and seeks and holds a selected VOR radial or heading while climbing, descending, or cruising. It maintains a precise altitude, automatically intercepts and locks on an ILS beam, and automatically compensates for crosswinds.

A Mach trim compensator is a part of the autopilot. The Model 23 and its later cousins, similar to other jets, exhibit a nose-down pitching characteristic when the wing's center of lift moves aft at high Mach numbers and altitudes. The phenomenon is called Mach tuck. Although Mach tuck in a Lear Jet is quite mild compared to many jets, it does degrade pitch stability somewhat. To prevent this from occurring, the autopilot's Mach trim system rolls in a small amount of nose-up trim at an appropriate speed to maintain the airplane's flying qualities, synchronizing attitude commands through the autopilot's pitch axis. It's activated when the airspeed is Mach .79 or higher and the pilot pushes a Mach trim engage button on the autopilot control panel. With the Mach trim compensator, General Electric-powered 20 Series airplanes are certified to fly at a Mach .82 maximum speed.

The autopilot also features a dual yaw damper system to damp oscillations of the airplane about its yaw axis, improving directional stability. To assure passengers of the smoothest possible ride, the yaw damper is normally activated immediately after takeoff and left engaged for the entire flight. Dual channels provide redundancy for safety. The 20 Series is required to have both yaw dampers operational to be legal for flight (because of its potentially unforgiving Dutch roll characteristics).

Through its Jet Electronics & Technology (J.E.T.) subsidiary, Lear Jet-manufactured components aboard the airplane included the autopilot, attitude instruments, nosewheel steering electronics, remote vertical and directional gyros, inverters, avionic control systems, and other electronic devices used for control and instrument purposes. All these devices were designed and built in J.E.T.'s Grand Rapids facility.

Worldwide Records—and Some Accidents

On May 21, 1965, a Model 23 established three official world speed records in a dramatic "dawn to dusk" transcontinental flight from Los Angeles to New York City and back. The 5,005-mile trip was completed in 10 hours and 21 minutes flying time, with the crew making an eastbound refueling stop in Wichita and a westbound one in Tulsa.

The 14th day of December 1965 saw another Model 23, straight off the Wichita production line, zoom to 40,000 feet in seven minutes and 21 seconds. It established a new business "time-to-climb" record. The feat, accomplished all the way on autopilot in adverse weather with seven persons aboard, demonstrated the airplane's ability to climb rapidly over rough weather conditions.

By the end of 1965, over eighty Model 23s had been sold. December of that year was a banner month for the Lear Jet Corporation—14 Model 23 deliveries were made. The company had the biggest sales month in its history. Bill Lear had beaten them all. The old-line general aviation manufacturers hadn't budged an inch. They'd believed Lear fail. Only Cessna would later see fit to produce a jet for business, and even that event would not occur until the latter part of 1968.

The company continued to break both airplane sales and flight speed records. Lear Jet crews were unofficially smashing a lot of other records during everyday business flights. The airplane had proved to be a true speedster; but the glory of the early speed-setting achievements had a somber side: fatal accidents.

October 21, 1965, saw the aircraft's first fatal accident occur at altitude not far from Jackson, Michigan. It involved Model 23 N804LJ, a demonstrator airplane still owned by Lear Jet. In an almost vertical, screaming dive, the airplane had augered its way into the ground after taking off from Detroit just minutes earlier. Falling uncontrollably out of the sky, it slammed into the ground at high speed. The nearly new airplane dug a crater eight feet deep, 45 feet long, and 15 feet wide. Small pieces of the airplane, few larger than a human hand, were strewn half a mile across the landscape. The experienced pilot, an employee of Lear Jet, had been flying the ship out of the Detroit airport after dropping off a Lear Jet executive. Following a lengthy investigation, the National Transportation Safety Board (NTSB) determined that the probable cause was loss of control "resulting from ac electrical power failure under night, instrument conditions." During its short life, N804LJ had experienced a number of electrical system problems. Whether or not any of them was positively the cause of the disaster could not be determined.

The following month, on November 14, a second fatal crash of the Model 23 occurred near Palm Springs, California. The NTSB later ruled the crash of this ship, N243F, to be caused by "spatial disorientation of the pilot, resulting in a loss of control." Although a veteran of larger propeller-driven transports, the pilot had little Lear Jet experience. His proficiency in the jet was described as "extremely marginal." The young private pilot accompanying him in the right seat could offer little help while the Model 23 was circling in and out of cloud cover high above the mountainous desert terrain while awaiting an enroute ATC clearance. Without warning, the airplane slipped from view on the controller's radar screen. A wisp of black smoke over the nearby Chocolate Mountains told the story: hitting the ground at high speed, virtually nothing from the airplane was recognizable in the bottom of the smoldering crater it dug.

The accidents had a sobering effect around the Lear Jet plant. The causes were ambiguous at best. Lear's engineers did their best to eliminate as many of the possible causes as they could. Elevator hinge problems, electrical system failures, and inadequate pilot training all surfaced as possible culprits in the crashes.

A total of 104 Model 23s were built. Serial numbers of the first 99 were 23-001 through 23-099. Five additional airplanes were also built, designated by an "A" after the serial number: 028, 045, 050, 065, and 082.

The Model 24 Sets Airline Standards

When the Model 23 ushered in practical, personal jet transportation for the world's executives, it came without a number of the safety features found aboard commercial jetliners. In addition, the 12,500-pound weight limit of the Model 23 was proving impractical. Lear originally certificated the jet under CAR 23 (which had a 12,500-pound limit) because he wanted customers to be able to fly the airplane with a single pilot. However, operator experience showed that most opted to fly the airplane with two pilots anyway.

Since the Model 23's type certificate had been issued, CAB licensing requirements for low capacity jet aircraft had been eased, allowing Bill Lear to take advantage of the structural strength of the 23's basic design to expand its gross weight. The airplane could then be used for charter and commuter airline use. His engineers developed a variant of the airplane, complying with FAR 25 transport category standards and offering operators a gross weight of 13,000 pounds. Designated the Lear Jet Model 24, the new airplane was announced to the aviation press in October 1965. In addition to its higher gross weight capabilities, the 24 incorporated many other safety-oriented improvements, including an improved, solid bird-proof windshield and increased cabin pressure differential for more comfortable high altitude operation. The electrical system had been extensively redesigned and incorporated a standby dry cell battery to prevent the possibility of total in-flight electrical failure, suspected in the Michigan crash. If all else should ever fail, the battery would power essential instruments, lights, and avionics. An independent standby attitude indicator was also provided. To guard against engine fires, a fire detection and extinguishing system was installed in each engine nacelle. An alcohol system for deicing was added to both pilot and copilot windshields. Vortex generators were installed on only the top surface of the wing, and strakes were added to the tip tanks. Better brakes rounded out the list of improvements. On February 24, 1966, the Model 24 took to the skies over Wichita for the first time. On March 17, it was awarded an FAA type certificate. By the middle of March, the Wichita assembly lines had already been converted for production of this latest variant of the Lear Jet.

The fatal Michigan and California crashes had left Bill Lear unsettled and confused. The exact causes had not been determined. On April 23, 1966, a third fatal crash added to that anguish. Over the plains of Clarendon, Texas, Model 23 N235R, owned by Rexall Drug and Chemical Company, suddenly fell out of the sky and plunged into the earth after plummeting uncontrollably for over six miles. The plane was flying in and out of clouds with moderate to severe turbulence. Upon issuing its report of the investigation, the NTSB ruled the cause as electrical failure or "loss of control of the aircraft, in turbulent, instrument conditions, which could have been caused by a failure of both gyro horizons." In fact, the Lear-remanufactured gyros were proving unreliable to many customers, substantiating the NTSB's suspicion as to the cause of the crash.

By now, the three fatal accidents and a series of landing mishaps caused more than ill feeling and uncertainty around the Wichita plant. The crashes also caused Lear Jet Corporation stock to drop almost 25 percent in value.

Total electrical failure was suspected in at least two of the crashes, so Lear Jet engineers developed the dry-cell type of standby battery system for retrofit to all Lear Jet airplanes. The system provided limited current to essential aircraft systems, such as the gyros, hydraulic solenoids, communications radios, and instrument lights. An independent J.E.T. standby vertical gyro, featuring a high-inertia gyro rotor to sustain erection in the event of power failure, was installed in the instrument panel to provide pilots with attitude information should the two electromechanical vertical gyro displays malfunction. The suspected electrical failure was an embarrassment for Bill Lear; he had built his aviation career in the electronics field. The aircraft's electrical and electronic systems were expected to excel in the industry. The fatal crashes stopped as pilots took more care in flying the aerial "hot rod" and as minor, but significant to safety, design improvements were incorporated into the ships.

Beating the Jet Commander Around the World

In times of crisis, Bill Lear, more than anyone, recognized the need for positive publicity. The opportunity presented itself when he found out that an around-the-world flight for the Jet Commander was in the planning stage. By now, Lear Jet and Jet Commander were fierce competitors. The Commander was slower, heavier, and more costly; but if it flew around the world, and set a world record in the process, it could bring irreparable harm to Lear Jet's reputation. The already lagging order backlog could disappear entirely.

The Model 23 crashes, along with slowing sales, prompted Lear to immediate action when he was told of Aero Commander's plans. He decided to take the Lear Jet around the world first. After he failed to get entertainer Arthur Godfrey to pilot the record flight, Lear gave Hank Beaird one week to get a production Model 23 ready. The Jet Commander flight had been planned for about a year, and Godfrey had earlier committed himself to joining the Jet Commander crew. Lear was angry at Godfrey and more committed than ever to beating the Jet Commander's attempt.

On May 26, 1966, a standard production Model 23, N427LJ, took off from Wichita for an attempt on the world record for an around-the-world flight. The crew was comprised of John Lear (Bill's younger son), Hank Beaird (Lear Jet chief test pilot), and Rick King (Lear Jet pilot and former Air Force fighter pilot). Journalist John Zimmerman also joined the flight crew, functioning as the official on-board observer. Before arriving back in Wichita, N427LJ would travel 22,993 miles during its 50 hour, 19 minute flight.

The mayor of Wichita, John Stevens, and governor of Kansas, William Avery, greeted the exhausted pilots upon their return. The previous around-the-world record had been set by a military version of the Boeing 707 six months earlier. It had flown at an average speed of 420.66 miles per hour. A Lear Jet statement said that "the flight, with only normal preparation and advance arrangements, demonstrates the vast worldwide mobility provided by the modern business jet."

A Fuselage Stretch Boosts Sales

In early 1966, Bill Lear authorized development work on the Lear Jet Model 25, which featured a fuselage stretch of 4 feet 2 inches and provided a cabin large enough to accommodate eight passengers and a crew of two. It was certified for both flight at 45,000 feet and known icing conditions. August 12, 1966, saw the first flight of the prototype Model 25.

After Gates Rubber purchased controlling interest in Lear Jet in April of 1967, increased emphasis was placed on product development. On October 10 of that year, the "stretched" Model 25 was awarded an FAA type certificate and certificated to FAR Part 25 transport category standards. That same day, the 25 was flown to the annual meeting of the National Business Aircraft Association. Predictably, the airplane created a stir with corporate pilots and aviation department managers. Acceptance by NBAA members was all important to its success in the marketplace. In particular, they liked the Model 25's interior appointments and operational flexibility. Because it was essentially a Model 24 with a fuselage stretch, production startup was relatively simple. Assembly operations soon began in Wichita, alongside its Model 24 sister ships.

On February 20, 1968, a standard Model 25, straight off the production line, flew to 40,000 feet in six minutes, 19 seconds, eclipsing the former "time-to-climb" record set by a Model 23. With its additional payload capacity, and well-publicized performance, the Model 25 was an instant hit. There was equal interest from domestic and international prospective customers. During February, the company announced the first Model 25 sales outside the U.S.—one to a Swiss industrialist and one to the government of the Republic of the Congo.

On September 25, 1968, the company announced the 13,500 pound gross weight Model 24B. The 24B featured an uprated 2,950 pound thrust CJ610-6 engine to carry increased payload. Certified for known icing conditions, the 24B featured electrothermal horizontal stabilizer deicing and radome alcohol anti-icing systems. On December 17th, the 24B was awarded an FAA type certificate.

A Model 25D cruises past Big Dome in Yosemite National Park. Learjet Corp.

Gates Makes a Few Changes

The biggest change involving the public's perception of the company occurred during 1968, when the name of Lear Jet Industries, Inc. was changed to Gates Learjet. All models of the "Lear Jet" would henceforth be known as "Learjets."

On May 5, 1970, the FAA gave its approval for Category II operations of the Learjet. This action would permit properly equipped Learjets to land in weather minimums of a 100-foot ceiling and 1,200-foot runway visual range. Bill Lear had always wanted his airplane to land under minimums so low a pilot would have to "get clearance from the Bureau of Mines" to land. At last, the airplane was certified as symbolically having that capability.

Under Gates' ownership, the company pushed evolutionary product improvement as the key to solidifying its market position. On July 17, 1970, the FAA awarded certification for the Model 24D, an advanced version of the 24B, itself an upgrade of the Model 24. Simultaneously, the Model 24B was dropped from the company's product line. A variant designated the 24C was still under development.

Model 25 crews continued to grab performance records whenever they could. On August 30, 1970, the new Model 25C, the latest variant at the time, established a new roundtrip speed record for all classes of commercial aircraft. The airplane flew straight from Los Angeles to New York, refueled, then streaked again across the country nonstop on the return leg of the 5,000 mile route. Elapsed time was 11 hours and 23 minutes. This flight also set new business jet speed records in each direction. On September 4, 1970, the Models 25B and 25C were awarded FAA type certificates. A longer-range version of the 25B, the 25C incorporated an additional 193 U.S. gallon fuel tank located in the fuselage to provide a 2,500 mile range. It also complied with stringent FAR 36 noise standards without the need to incorporate thrust-robbing engine exhaust noise suppressors. The same 2,950 pound thrust CJ610-6 engines installed in the Model 24 were used. This Model 25 later became available with the CJ610-8A engine, allowing operation up to 51,000 feet, a first for any business jet.

In December of 1970 the company abandoned development work on the Model 24C. The Model 24D was simultaneously introduced in its place. The 24D offered increased fuel capacity for extended range and greater payload capacity. The nonstructural bullet at the junction of the horizontal and vertical tail surfaces was deleted on the 24D and all subsequent Learjets. The rounded cabin windows of earlier airplanes were replaced with square units. The 24D was later redesignated the Model 24D/A.

The 13,500 pound gross weight 24E was the last variant of the Model 24 ever built. Incorporating CJ610-8A engines, with new fuel controls and tail pipes, it was certified for flight at 51,000 feet.

A Model 25C made a nonstop flight from Wichita to Caracas, Venezuela, on February 28, 1971. It covered the 2,720 miles in five hours and 30 minutes. With three persons on board, it landed with a respectable 40 minutes of fuel remaining.

The 500th Learjet, a Model 24D, was delivered to the Navy of Mexico on April 8, 1975. Gates Learjet had now extended its lead over its nearest competitor by 170 airplanes.

A turbojet engine, such as the original CJ610, works best at high altitude, while fan-equipped airplanes perform most efficiently at somewhat lower flight levels. As a result, fan-equipped Learjets do not cruise as high as their GE-powered sister ships. For those operators who desired the high-altitude "Learjet Country" performance of the Model 24, even during the fanjet era, continual improvement and production of that model was undertaken. On October 28, 1975, all Model 24 variants were superseded by the 24E and 24F, part of the Century III series announced by the company. These new models featured a new cambered wing, a new stall warning system, and other aerodynamic improvements to reduce stall and approach speeds and balanced field length requirements. The improvements were also retrofittable on earlier model airplanes. The basic difference between the two models was fuel capacity: the 24E carried 715 gallons, while the 24F featured 840 gallons to achieve greater range.

On September 26, 1977, the so-called "Longhorn" series was unveiled by Gates Learjet marketers with the flight of a General Electric-powered Longhorn 28 at Houston's Hobby Airport. It was the day before the opening of the National Business Aircraft Association annual meeting in Houston. The unique shape of the airplane's new "winglets" was the reason for calling the ship the Longhorn. By significantly reducing the wing's induced drag (normally produced by the wingtip vortex), the Longhorn series would offer operators increased range with no increase in fuel capacity. Research indicated that during cruise flight, winglets could reduce induced drag by about 20 percent, which would result in flying a lot further on the same amount of fuel. Beside providing greatly enhanced fuel efficiency and performance, the Model 28 would be the only business jet capable of climbing directly to a 51,000-foot cruise altitude.

The Longhorn modifications had first been flown out of Wichita on a standard Model 25 fuselage on August 24, 1977. To expedite the airplane's test program, a prototype wing had been fitted to a standard Model 25 fuselage. The Model 28 was basically a Model 25 modified with a new long-span wing, having supercritical winglets at the tips in place of the usual wingtip fuel tanks. The Model 28 received its FAA type certificate on January 30, 1979, but only five 28s were delivered that year. The Model 28 carried two pilots and eight passengers and had a total fuel capacity of 702 gallons. The Model 29, a derivative of the 28, carried only six passengers but stored an extra 100 gallons of fuel for additional range. Attractive to many operators, both Models 28 and 29 powered by CJ610-8A engines, were approved for high-altitude "Learjet Country" operation.

With a long succession of vastly upgraded variants of Bill Lear's original design now history, the Model 23 was slowly slipping into oblivion. On April 1, 1978, a Model 23, considered by many to be the world's first true business jet aircraft, was made a permanent exhibit in the new general aviation gallery of the Smithsonian Institution's National Air and Space Museum in Washington, D.C. The airplane was suspended from the ceiling of the mammoth exhibit hall, where countless visitors would see Bill Lear's timeless creation. Sadly, the Lear Jet was removed from its perch years later because of space limitations and is currently on display at a museum in Richmond, Virginia. Four months after the Lear Jet went on display at the Smithsonian, another Model 23 (serial number 23-023) became the first airplane of its type to top 10,000 hours of flight time.

On January 29, 1979, the FAA awarded certification papers for the Model 28/29 Longhorn series, making it the world's first production aircraft to have winglets. Unfortunately, only a handful of Model 28/29 aircraft were produced before weak demand caused discontinuance of the line. However, the viability of using winglets for business jets had been proven through the 28's extensive flight trials.

Kitty Hawk, North Carolina, birthplace of aviation, saw another significant aviation event take place on February 21, 1979. Former astronaut Neil A. Armstrong, a Gates

Learjet board member at the time, and P. T. (Pete) Reynolds, currently Learjet's chief of engineering flight test, smashed five world records for business jets when the Model 28 they were co-piloting climbed above 50,000 feet in a little over 12 minutes after breaking ground.

The Learjet Becomes Safer

Learjet accidents were still a problem. The airplane had to be flown faster than other jets on approach and landing, causing safety concerns and occasional mishaps. Gates Learjet engineers wanted to lower the stall speed without affecting high speed performance. The result of their engineering and flight test work was the Century III modification to the airplane's wing. The modified wing generated more lift at higher angles of attack than the airfoil used on earlier model Learjets. Best of all, there was no overall drag penalty even though it had a blunter leading edge. The Century III model airplanes, and earlier models retrofitted with the leading edge, exhibited lowered stall and approach speeds. The result was a big reduction in takeoff and landing distance without degrading high speed performance.

The Century III wing modification calls for reshaping the leading edge of the wing using an airfoil profile developed by NASA in the early sixties. The camber of the wing is recontoured from the leading edge back to the second of the wing's eight spars. Effectiveness of the profile had been proven during testing in 1967. Using for testing the second Learjet ever built, engineers mounted the entire jet in the cavernous NASA Ames Laboratory wind tunnel at Moffett Field. Also part of the Century III modification was a new stall rate sensor to more accurately sense the entry rate into a stall. By the middle of 1976, the first production Models 24 and 25, along with the fanjet-powered Models 35A and 36A, were being delivered to customers as Century III series Learjets. Airplanes produced prior to introduction of the Century III series could also be retrofitted with the new leading edge.

The Dee Howard Company and The Raisbeck Group joined forces in the mid-1970s to develop the Howard/Raisbeck Mark II handling improvement package of modifications for the Models 24 and 25. The Howard company is an acknowledged leader in the modification and conversion of executive and airline aircraft. The Raisbeck Group was founded in 1974 by the engineers who developed the high-lift systems for many Boeing, McDonnell Douglas, and Robertson aircraft.

The Mark II system modification included new strakes at the wingtip tanks to enhance aileron response during slow speed and engine-out operation. Pilots appreciated this while flying in crosswinds or gusty conditions. New-technology wing leading edges were installed over the first five percent of the wing chord. These full-span, high-lift, low-drag leading edges introduced aerodynamic wing twist across the span, reducing or eliminating upper surface shock waves at cruise speed. The leading edge significantly reduced stall speeds and cruise drag.

An improved angle of attack indicator system, marked in degrees for use both in cruise and during low speed flight, was included as part of the Mark II system. The airplane's existing stick shaker and pusher systems were retained. However, they were reset for optimum performance, complementing the Mark II's natural aerodynamic stall warning capability and improved stall characteristics. A new flap position sensor and indicator made accurate flap setting easier than on unmodified airplanes. Because of reduced shock strength, the wing's vortex generators were no longer needed. This cut cruise drag and made the airplane more responsive to aileron movements at low speeds.

Other Mark II modifications included a new flap pre-select system to provide greater convenience in selecting flap positions. A new flap-actuated pitch trim system automatically put an ''up'' preload on the elevators as the flaps were deflected. This eliminated most stabilizer trim changes during clean-up from takeoff to cruise and during transition to final approach. A new contour on the flap trailing edges provided greater efficiency for takeoff and landing. Rounding out the modification package, new aileron gap seals stopped lower-surface air from bleeding through the upper surface, increasing aileron effectiveness at low speed and reducing drag at cruise speed.

In October of 1979, another Gates Learjet advanced handling package was certified by the FAA for the Model 24. Also designed to improve Learjet stall characteristics, the ''Softflite'' system would become standard on all future production Learjets.

In June of 1982, the first production Model 25G entered service and immediately broke long-distance speed and fuel consumption records. A series of demonstration flights dramatically proved the new 25G's ability to fly farther and faster and use less fuel than earlier Model 20 Series airplanes. The 25G was the culmination of a lengthy joint engineering development effort between Gates Learjet Corporation and the Dee Howard Company of San Antonio, Texas. The Howard company simultaneously introduced a retrofit kit for earlier Model 25s to bring them up to 25G performance standards. Incorporating what was learned during a lengthy flight test program, major drag reduction was achieved, which significantly improved handling qualities and stall characteristics.

On September 28, 1983, the FAA certified ''Softflite I,'' the wing modification developed for earlier Models 23 and 24. Certification of the package for the Model 25 had been completed in November of 1982. All Learjet 20 Series airplanes could now enjoy improved slow flight handling characteristics by installing the Softflite I retrofit kit.

The airplane that once behaved like a scalded cat on approach and landing was now purring like a kitten. At last, the engineers had succeeded in taking the bite out of the Learjet without touching its high-end performance.

Featuring winglets and upgraded engines, Models 28 and 29 exemplified the ultimate turbojet-powered Learjet; but with almost the entire free world's airline fleet now flying fanjet-powered airliners, it was time for Gates Learjet to adapt the turbofan engine to the Learjet. The next chapter in the Learjet's development was about to unfold.

4
Learjet's 30 Series Ushers in Fanjet Power

Evolution of the business jet followed essentially the same path as that of commercial jet transports. The Boeing 707 and DC-8 started their lives as turbojet-powered airliners. After Pratt & Whitney fitted a fan section to its basic JT3 turbojet engine back in the early 1960s, the 707 and DC-8 became the first fanjet-powered airliners. The airlines soon discovered that a turbofan, or fanjet, engine is far more efficient than a turbojet one.

In a turbojet engine, such as the General Electric CJ610, the turbine section extracts only enough gas stream energy necessary to drive the engine compressor section, accessory gearbox, and engine-driven accessories. The remaining gas stream is forced through the exhaust nozzle to produce jet thrust. In a turbofan engine, by contrast, gas stream energy is used to rotate a fan (essentially a fixed pitch shrouded propeller), compressor, and engine-driven accessories. Sufficient gas flow energy remains to provide jet thrust through the engine's exhaust nozzle.

In principle, a turbofan engine operates the same as a turboprop engine, except that the turboprop's propeller is replaced by an axial-flow fan enclosed in a duct. On some turbofans, the fan assembly is a part of the first-stage compressor blades. In the case of the Learjet's TFE731 turbofan, it's mounted as a separate fan blade assembly.

The turbofan engine was developed to convert more fuel energy into thrust. With more of that fuel energy converted into pressure, an increase in efficiency is achieved. A major turbofan advantage is that the engine produces additional thrust without increasing the fuel burn. The end result is savings in fuel with a corresponding increase in aircraft range.

Because the turbofan converts more fuel energy into pressure, another turbine stage must be added to generate power for driving the fan assembly and to increase the gas expansion through the engine's turbine section. That is, there is less energy remaining after the turbine that drives the fan extracts power—leaving less pressure at the back of the turbine. Also, the engine's jet nozzle itself has to be larger in area. With these restrictions, the "core" of a turbofan engine doesn't develop as much jet nozzle thrust as a comparable pure turbojet. However, the fan section more than compensates for the dropoff in thrust developed by the core. Depending on the design of individual fan assemblies, fans produce approximately 50 percent of a turbofan engine's total thrust.

Two different duct designs are used with forward-fan engines, whose fans are located forward of the engine's compressor section. The air leaving the fan can be ducted overboard, or it can be ducted along the outer case of the engine's core to be discharged through the tail pipe's jet nozzle. The fan air is either mixed with the engine exhaust gases before it's discharged or is passed directly to the atmosphere without prior mixing.

The turbofan engine represents a compromise between the excellent efficiency and high-thrust capability of a turboprop engine and the high-speed, high-altitude capability of a turbojet. Compared to a turbojet engine, the turbofan's fan section moves far more air and at lower velocities. In addition to producing an appreciable amount of thrust itself, the TFE731 engine's fan directs its airflow around the core of the engine before mixing with the turbine exhaust gases at the rear. The fan moves the large volume of air at a much lower velocity than the gases traveling through the core of the engine. The fan's airflow cools the engine core, reducing the final velocity of the gases leaving the engine's tail pipe. A turbofan delivers the same amount of thrust produced by a turbojet, but with less fuel expended to achieve it—that is, a turbofan produces more power (in thrust pounds) for each pound of fuel burned than its pure jet counterpart. Plus, turbofan engines produce far less noise as a by-product of their operation than pure jets do. The reduced velocity of exhaust gases leaving the tail pipe accounts for this secondary benefit. In addition to aircraft performance gains, noise reduction has become the principal fanjet benefit under stringent FAR Part 36 noise regulations.

When the Lear Jet and Jet Commander first appeared on the scene, they were powered by General Electric CJ610 pure jets; but when the Garrett Corporation of Phoenix, Arizona, announced development of the TFE731 turbofan engine for business aircraft in the late 1960s, practically every business jet manufacturer in the world expressed interest in the efficient small turbine. In addition to the Learjet, the Commodore Jet, Falcon 10, Sabreliner, Jetstar, and DH-125 were all adapted to the TFE731 engine. The engine's performance and low noise level became so popular that retrofit kits were developed and sold for the Jetstar and de Havilland DH-125.

Availability of the TFE731 led directly to the introduction of the Learjet Models 35 and 36 in 1973. Gates Learjet originally planned to develop the aircraft as fanjet-powered variants of the Model 25, with the designations 25B-GF and 25C-GF. The "GF" stood for "Garrett Fan." The TFE731 promised to reduce the Learjet's takeoff noise levels and specific fuel consumption (SFC) well below that of the CJ610, which had been the standard Learjet powerplant for almost a decade.

TFE731 Design Features

The TFE731 is a lightweight, "two-spool" turbofan engine that is modularized for ease of maintenance. Two spools mean that there are two independent compressor-turbine sections, each rotating separately on concentric shafts. A spinner hub and axial flow fan comprise the fan section. A four-stage axial low pressure compressor and three-stage low-pressure turbine comprise the low pressure spool on the engine. A single-stage centrifugal high pressure compressor, driven by a single-stage axial high pressure turbine, is mounted on the same shaft. All shaft-driven accessories are driven by the high pressure compressor gear train. The spool shafts are concentric, with the low pressure spool shaft passing through the center of the high pressure spool shaft. The TFE731's reverse flow annular combustor configuration allows the turbine to be placed near the compressor it

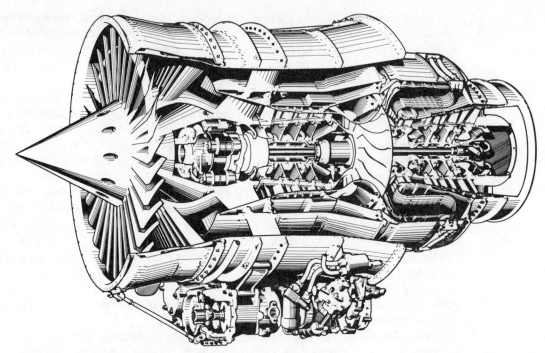

Cutaway view of Garrett TFE731 turbofan engine showing major components. Garrett Turbine Engine Co.

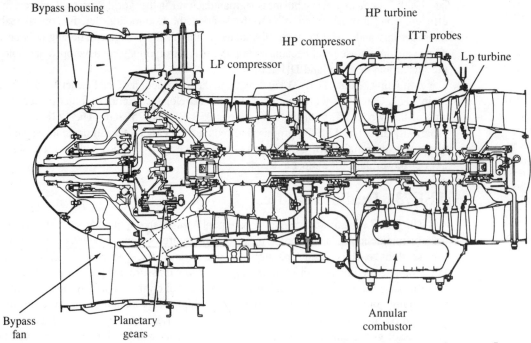

Sectional view of TFE731 engine. Note large fan section, concentric rotor shafting, and reverse flow combustor. Garrett Turbine Engine Co.

drives, shortening the overall length of the engine. The arrangement also ensures that the external turbine section skin surfaces remain relatively cool.

The TFE731 was designed to incorporate components and design concepts developed for other Garrett gas turbine units, including auxiliary power units and turboprop engines. The low pressure compressor, for example, makes use of a design developed for the Boeing 747's onboard GTCP 660-4 auxiliary power unit (APU). The TFE731's shaft components were inherited from the TSCP 700-4 onboard APU for the McDonnell Douglas DC-10 jetliner. The engine's second-stage compressor wheel uses a shape developed for Garrett's TPE331 turboprop engine used to power a wide variety of propeller-driven business aircraft.

Garrett design engineers chose a gear reduction drive for the fan assembly. This provides fewer engine turbine stages and a smaller engine diameter than a more conventional straight turbine drive shaft approach offers. The gearing drives the four-stage axial compressor at a higher speed than would be possible if the compressor were mounted on the same shaft driving the fan. Without the geared fan, the turbine would be forced to rotate at a lower speed, requiring additional stages with a larger diameter turbine to accomplish the same amount of work. In the TFE731-2 engine, the high-pressure spool is driven at about 28,942 rpm while maximum fan speed is 10,967. Another reason for Garrett's selection of the geared-fan configuration was to allow use of the existing Boeing 747 APU compressor section for the TFE731.

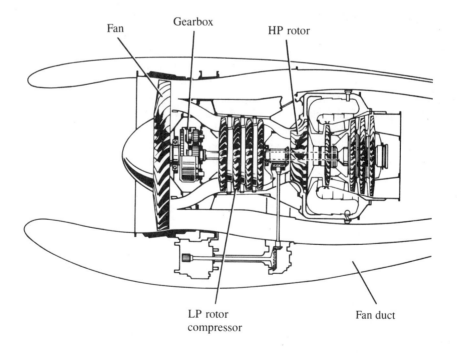

Cross-sectional view of TFE731 and nacelle structure revealing major dynamic components. Note annular passage where fan air flows aft along outside skin of engine's core. Garrett Turbine Engine Co.

During development of the TFE731, a key objective was to design an engine that could meet both current and projected noise and emission criteria. The reverse flow combustor not only shortens the engine's length, but also reduces pollutants discharged from the engine. This combustor produces reduced exhaust emissions because fuel travels through a longer flow path in the combustor, providing a more homogeneous mixture of the injected fuel. The result is a lean overall fuel-air ratio in the primary combustion zone, which minimizes oxygen deficient zones. Emission reductions also result from a high volume-to-surface ratio in the combustor, which minimizes quenching of raw fuel on the combustor walls. Noise pollution has been reduced by the use of a carefully selected fan bypass ratio and the elimination of inlet guide vanes.

TFE731 Testing at Gates Learjet

Because the TFE731 engine itself was new and one of its first civil applications would be the first fanjet-equipped Learjet, an extensive flight testing program was accomplished by Gates Learjet prior to certification of the Model 35 and a longer-range variant, the Model 36. A Model 25 test airplane, N661LJ, was converted for use as a testbed for the 3,500 pound thrust TFE731-2 engine. The Garrett engine was mounted in the starboard nacelle, retaining the standard CJ610 engine in the existing port nacelle. Because the TFE731 nacelle has a larger circumference to accommodate the engine's fan section, the test airplane took on a lopsided appearance. To hold the new engine, an all-new engine mount system was needed along with a complete redesign of the engine pylon. This test airplane first flew during May of 1971, ushering in the fanjet era at Gates Learjet. A second Model 25 test airplane, featuring two TFE731-2s, joined the first one in flight trials on January 4, 1973.

Because the airframe and airframe systems of Models 35 and 36 required relatively minor modification of the existing turbojet-powered Model 25 systems, engineering development and flight testing of the fanjet versions progressed smoothly. A definitive Model 35 prototype first took off from Wichita's runway on August 22, 1973. A week later, the Models 35 and 36 were both unveiled during a press conference and showing for prospective customers in Wichita. Gates Learjet marketing executives stressed the aircraft's dramatically improved range/payload and cost effectiveness. Marrying the proven Learjet airframe with twin Garrett TFE731-2 turbofan engines made it all possible.

Differences between Models 35 and 36

Compared to the Model 25, both new fanjet-powered models featured a 13-inch increase in overall length and a 2-foot extension to each wingtip, outboard of the ailerons. Both the Models 35 and 36 were certificated at a 17,000-pound maximum weight, but differed in fuel and seating capacities. The Model 35 featured a transcontinental range, storing 921 U.S. gallons and carrying eight passengers. The Model 35 can carry eight passengers and their luggage from New York to San Francisco nonstop. It can also fly from San Francisco to Hawaii nonstop, bucking headwinds and still landing in Hawaii with a full fuel reserve. The Model 36 surrenders two passenger seats to accommodate additional fuel tanks in the aft fuselage. This brings the airplane's fuel capacity up to 1,109 gallons, providing nonstop transatlantic capability. The Model 36 can fly across the North Atlantic, against headwinds, and land with full reserves.

Garrett TFE731-2-2B engine powers Models 35A, 36A, and 31. Garrett Turbine Engine Co.

Certification of the Models 35 and 36 occurred on July 9, 1974. Shortly thereafter, initial deliveries took place, with Mesa Petroleum of Amarillo, Texas, becoming the first corporate owner on December 11, 1974.

On April 5, 1975, a standard-equipped Model 36 completed a nonstop, 3,833-mile flight from Hawaii to Wichita in only seven hours and 15 minutes, capping a 25,000-mile demonstration tour of Europe and the Middle East. The flight, believed to be the longest nonstop distance ever flown in a standard production model general aviation aircraft, was accomplished with two passengers aboard in addition to the crew. The airplane had just completed an 8,350-mile trip from Paris to Hawaii in 19 hours and 51 minutes, with stops in Canada and Los Angeles.

During the 1975 fiscal year, a record 93 new Gates Learjets were delivered. The total included an industry milestone of 21 units delivered in April. One of these was the 600th Learjet, a Model 35. It was delivered to Dart Industries, an early Learjet owner. The late Justin Dart was a longtime friend of Bill Lear.

In 1976, the Century III package of aerodynamic improvements developed for the 20 Series Learjets, particularly the new wing designed to improve low-speed handling, refined the Models 35A and 36A. Each model has a gross weight of 18,000 pounds.

Typical Model 35 seating arrangement with refreshment area located at the right, near the center of the cabin. Moya Olsen Lear collection.

Other changes included thrust reversers and the new J.E.T. FC-530 autopilot. A still higher gross weight option, increasing the weight to 18,300 pounds, was also offered for the 35A. Between May 17 and 19 of 1976, a Model 36, captained by renowned golfer-businessman-pilot Arnold Palmer, made an historic American bicentennial around-the-world flight, establishing a business jet speed record for a global flight of 57 hours, 25 minutes and 42 seconds. Palmer averaged a speed of 400.23 miles per hour.

The Model 35's TFE731 engines are pylon-mounted on the aft fuselage near the air-craft center line, just as on earlier Learjets. Each provides 3,500 pounds of thrust. The pylon firewalls are fabricated from stainless steel for fire protection. Each engine has a fire warning system, firewall shutoff valves to isolate combustible fluids, and a nacelle fire extinguishing system. Engine cowlings are easily removable to allow full access to all engine-mounted accessories and components.

The engine itself is divided into seven inspection zones, based on component location and accessibility within the engine. The zones are inspected at intervals appropriate to the components they contain. A time between overhaul (TBO) is assigned to modules within

Many Learjets fly the world's airways during the late night hours as airfreighters. Note how this Model 35's entry door accommodates large parcels. Learjet Corp.

an inspection zone for which field maintenance may not be practical. The TBOs are compatible with zone inspection intervals so that modules can be changed during scheduled inspections. Repairs or replacement of components are made as necessary, with the engine remaining in service during the process.

Thrust Reversers Shorten Rollouts

Stopping a heavily loaded airplane on a slick or icy runway can be a nightmare for jet pilots. Reversible pitch propellers solved the problem for pilots of piston-engine and turboprop-powered airplanes. Commercial jet aircraft, however, must rely on good brakes, wheel anti-skid systems—and reversing the thrust produced by their engines. The high airspeeds and gross weights common to jet aircraft result in high wing loadings and increased landing speeds. In many cases, wheel brakes can't be entirely relied on to slow the airplane within a reasonable distance immediately after touchdown.

Thrust reversers can be divided into two categories: the mechanical-blockage type and the aerodynamic-blockage type. Mechanical blockage is accomplished by placing a removable obstruction in the exhaust gas stream at the rear of the exhaust nozzle. The engine exhaust gases are mechanically blocked and diverted at a suitable angle in the reverse direction by an inverted cone, half-sphere or other means of obstruction placed in a position to reverse the gas flow. In aerodynamic-blockage thrust reversers, thin airfoils or obstructions are placed in the gas stream, either along the length of the exhaust duct or immediately aft of the engine's exhaust nozzle.

Thrust reversers must not adversely affect engine operation, either during reverse or forward thrust modes. They must withstand high temperatures, be mechanically strong, relatively light in weight, reliable and fail-safe. When not in use, they must not add appreciably to the engine frontal area, being streamlined into the engine nacelle. To satisfy minimum braking requirements after touchdown, thrust reversers should be able to produce in reverse at least 50 percent of the full forward thrust that the engines can develop.

In 1978 a thrust reverser package developed by Aeronca Inc. became available on new Models 35As and 36As, or as a retrofit on earlier aircraft. Another thrust reverser system, designated the T/R-4000, was developed by Gates Learjet in association with The Dee Howard Company of San Antonio, Texas. This mechanical-blockage-type thrust reverser features light weight and low maintenance, with reverse thrust available within two seconds after touchdown. The T/R-4000 features its own hydraulic accumulator to allow operation even if the airplane's primary hydraulic system fails. If necessary, the thrust reverser for a single engine can be used alone.

At power lever positions below idle, the reverser operates to form a turning barrier in the path of the escaping exhaust gases. This, in turn, reverses the forward thrust of the

Dee Howard thrust reversers, as installed on Model 35A, in stowed position. Dee Howard Co.

Model 35A thrust reversers in deployed position for landing on slippery runways. Dee Howard Co.

engine, slowing the airplane during the landing rollout. Power lever positions below idle cause the engine to accelerate in controllable amounts up to full thrust. Either partial or full reverse thrust may be used at the pilot's discretion. When the reverser isn't in use, the clamshell doors retract and nest neatly around the engine to form the rear section of the engine nacelle.

An unimproved runway kit allows the Learjet to operate from unimproved runways, both sod and gravel. This option consists of a main landing gear snubber, a nosewheel spin-up kit, and a gravel guard kit. The snubber installation limits the rebound loads imparted to the main landing gear cylinder during sod-rough field operations. The spin-up device uses engine bleed air to pre-spin the nosewheel to a rotation rate corresponding to the aircraft's landing speed. This prevents gravel scatter at touchdown, minimizing the possibility of gravel ingestion in the engines. The gravel guard kit consists of protective coverings that fit over the landing lights, rotating beacon and on the underside of the flaps.

In the event the brakes and thrust reversers should both fail, the Learjet is offered with an optional drag chute system to stop the ship on the remaining runway length. The unit is installed in the airplane's tailcone access door and activated by a manual control handle located on the pilot's pedestal.

Military Variants of Model 35

In addition to its traditional interest in the business flying community, Gates Learjet pursued adapting the aircraft to military-style missions. Starting as early as the late 1960s, Bill Lear had envisioned developing special airborne capabilities outside the field of executive transport. With the advent of the Model 30 Series, true multi-mission military roles became possible. The versatile Model 35A, recognized for its range, speed, ceiling, and payload characteristics, became widely known for meeting a variety of airborne requirements including airways calibration, medical evacuation, stand-off reconnaissance, target towing, and electronic warfare.

On August 30, 1978, Gates Learjet announced that a special mission Model 35A had been developed that incorporated attachments under the wings for equipping the airplane with ejector racks and a variety of external stores. With highly sophisticated surveillance systems installed, the new Learjet variant was designed specifically for sea patrol.

The Model 35A's rugged wing structure accommodates stores of 1,000 pounds under each wing. Each wing structure is capable of withstanding loads up to nine Gs. This provides a wide safety margin for high speed maneuvering during combat exercises. The modified 35A offers up to five hours endurance and over 99 percent mission reliability.

Model 35A in a low pass over the Southwestern U.S. Learjet Corp.

Model 35As have been configured with electronic warfare jammers, chaff dispensers, tow target systems, reconnaissance radar, special cameras, and fire control radar. The Model 35A can be configured for a wide range of applications in a variety of configurations, including external wing stores, side-looking radar, air drop provisions, camera bays, atmospheric research devices, and other modifications tailored to specific needs.

Rivaling its reputation as an executive transport, the Model 35A also achieved recognition as a target-towing support aircraft. Equipped with a Marquardt MTR-101 reeling machine, the modified Model 35A provides tow cable lengths of up to 30,000 feet at speeds up to 350 knots. This permits relatively short cable lengths of a few thousand feet for air-to-air gunnery, as well as long tow lengths required for surface-to-air missile exercises. On September 3, 1984, the FAA certified the Marquardt MTR-101 system for operational use aboard Learjets.

At the 1979 Paris Air Show and 1980 Farnborough Show in England, a special missions version of the Models 35 and 36 was displayed. It was named the Learjet Sea Patrol. With a dash capability of about 500 miles per hour and low-speed maneuverability down to 130 miles per hour, Gates Learjet executives claimed that the Sea Patrol could provide twice the coverage, in the maritime patrol role, of a conventional medium-size twin turboprop maritime surveillance aircraft. Equipment that could be specified included Litton AN/APS-504(V)2 sea surveillance radar, low-light level television with video facility, forward-looking infrared sensors, and the Daedalus DS-1210 multi-spectral infrared and ultraviolet line scanner with associated data processing peripherals. ASW sonobuoy equipment could also be carried, and under each wing was a hardpoint to mount survival equipment pods, flares, or other loads up to 485 pounds.

On September 10, 1982, the Defense Forces of Finland took delivery of the first of three new special mission Model 35As in ceremonies at the Wichita plant. This aircraft order, valued at $18 million including spare parts, was a major milestone in Gates Learjet's expanding involvement in worldwide special mission aircraft operations. The specially engineered 35As were equipped with a variety of electronic surveillance systems, internally mounted long-range oblique photographic cameras, podded reconnaissance camera units, and externally mounted target-tow systems.

On May 26, 1983, Gates Learjet announced that it had signed a contract with the People's Republic of China for delivery of a new Model 30 Series airplane equipped with side-looking airborne radar (SLAR) manufactured by Goodyear Aerospace Corporation. The first Model 36A was delivered to the People's Republic of China on April 20, 1984.

U.S. Government authorities regard the Model 35A as a valuable military resource. This was evident when the Air Force selected it as its new operations support aircraft and leased a fleet of 80 aircraft.

Aerodynamic Improvements for the Model 35

The Century III package of product improvements developed for 20 Series airplanes centered about wing modifications designed to improve low speed handling. This led directly to introduction of the Models 35A and 36A in 1976.

In 1977, the Raisbeck Group obtained FAA approval for the Models 35 and 36 for its Mark IV Stall Characteristics Improvement System (SCIS). Intended as a retrofit package for these airplanes, this system consists of two leading-edge wing fences which alter the airflow patterns, reducing stalling speed by several knots. It also calls for removing the existing wing vortex generators. This provides a seven to 10 percent improvement in drag during cruise, with a corresponding increase in range. Gates Learjet achieved similar results with its own Softflite package, which became standard on all production aircraft delivered after July 1, 1979. The same year, a further enhancement became available for the Learjet 35A: a fifth cabin window on the port side and a sixth on the starboard side. On April 27, 1979, a Model 35A, the 900th aircraft to roll off the Gates Learjet assembly line, was delivered to the aerospace giant, McDonnell Douglas Corporation of St. Louis, Missouri.

Minimal cross-section of Model 35's cylindrical fuselage is graphically emphasized in this head-on shot. Learjet Corp.

From February 16th to 18th of 1983, a Model 35A, captained by businesswoman-pilot Brooke Knapp of California, set a new record for speed around the world of 50 hours, 22 minutes and 42 seconds total elapsed time. The flight eclipsed an official business jet weight class record set by a Model 24 in 1966. Undoubtedly, the Model 35A's aerodynamic enhancements did much to earn the new record.

The Learjet in Air Force Colors

On September 19, 1983, the Department of Defense awarded Gates Learjet a $175,403,178 fixed-price lease and contractor logistic support contract to supply and support 80 Model 35As for the U.S. Air Force's Operational Support Aircraft program. Designated the C-21A, the first of four aircraft a month was scheduled to be delivered during March 1984. Operated by the Military Airlift Command, the airplanes would deliver high priority and time-sensitive cargo and be used to train pilots and provide passenger airlift.

Gates Learjet Aircraft Service Corporation (GLASCO) was formed in February 1984, as a wholly owned subsidiary, to support the C-21A program. It furnished full logistic support at 16 locations around the world for the fleet of C-21As.

On March 13, 1984, six months after the lease contract was signed, Gates Learjet rolled out the first of the 80 new C-21A aircraft in ceremonies at the company's new corporate headquarters in Tucson. These aircraft were built in Wichita, but completed and delivered in Tucson.

The Learjet is drafted: the USAF C-21A variant of the Model 35A. Learjet Corp.

Generous size of cowling doors assures easy access to engine components on this USAF C-21A. Learjet Corp.

The Air Force C-21A marked its first service anniversary in April 1985 after Gates Learjet had delivered 52 airplanes—all on or ahead of schedule. In their first year, the C-21As accumulated more than 18,900 fleetwide flying hours and more than 20,000 take-offs and landings and achieved a "mission capable" rate of over 95 percent.

The 80th and final C-21A was delivered on schedule to the Air Force in October 1985. During the 19-month delivery program, Gates Learjet also trained 240 Air Force pilots who accrued more than 40,000 flying hours across the fleet.

On September 30, 1986, Gates Learjet and the Air Force reached an agreement on the purchase of the C-21A fleet for $180 million. It was the largest single sale in the 26-year history of the Learjet company. GLASCO was to continue maintaining the 80 aircraft under contract at various locations around the world. At the time of the sale, the C-21A fleet had logged over 95,000 accident-free flying hours.

The U.S. Air Force signed a $14 million contract for four C-21A airplanes for the Air National Guard on August 3, 1987. Assigned to Andrews Air Force Base in the Washington, D.C. area, two of the C-21As were to be delivered by mid-August and the maining two in September. Gates Learjet's subsidiary, GLASCO, negotiated a contract to provide spares support. GLASCO also supported the Air Force's C-21A fleet, which by that date had accumulated well over 100,000 hours of flying time.

Export Sales of 30 Series Learjets

The first Model U36A, which was actually a Model 36A with extensive modifications, was delivered to the Japan Maritime Self-Defense Force on January 9, 1986. The airplane was destined to be used for on-board radar training for the Japanese naval fleet. On January 15, 1987, the second Model U36A, a commercial Model 36A with extensive modifications, was delivered as part of a multi-year contract that extends into the 1990s.

The Brazilian Air Force signed a contract for three Model 35A special missions aircraft on December 12, 1986. The airplanes were to be modified by Gates Learjet to fly specialized survey operations. They were the first Learjet airplanes purchased by the Brazilian Air Force. On November 27, 1987, the Brazilian Air Force signed a contract for three additional Model 35As to be used as executive transports.

On August 25, 1987, the Royal Thai Air Force signed a contract for two Lear Model 35A special mission airplanes, which were to be modified by Gates Learjet for strategic reconnaissance and precision survey photography. The unique Thai Model 35As carried LOROP (Long Range Oblique Photographic) and large format vertical mapping cameras. They were also equipped with TACAN, INS, IFF, and radar warning receivers. The airplanes were configured with two 1,000-pound capacity wing hardpoints, capable of carrying infrared and radar electronic countermeasures and various two target systems. Deliveries were scheduled for early 1988.

Japanese Maritime Self Defense Force (JMSDF) Model U36A. Learjet Corp.

These Model 35As were the first business-class jets ever sold in Thailand. However, at the time, 24 governments and military organizations around the world were operating other Learjet models.

The Model 31 Makes Its Debut

The Model 31 was unveiled at the 40th National Business Aircraft Association annual meeting in New Orleans on September 29, 1987. Described as a "new kind of Learjet," the Model 31 was targeted at entry-level jet customers moving up from turboprop airplanes. The principal goals of the Model 31 development program, which began in July of 1986, were to simplify the airplane's systems, make the airplane handle more easily, and reduce pilot workload without sacrificing overall performance.

The Model 31's flight control system was simplified: the complex stick-pusher system was replaced by aerodynamic Delta Fins, an innovative new Learjet feature. Also, the Mach trim system and stick puller were no longer required. The 31 incorporates a J.E.T. FC-531 autopilot. Its hybrid design uses a digital outer servo loop together with an analog inner loop. The result is outstanding ride comfort and control quality. Standard autopilot features include all-angle intercept and extensive built-in self-test capabilities. Autopilot controls and annunciators are located on the aircraft's instrument panel glareshield.

Model 31 at altitude. Learjet Corp.

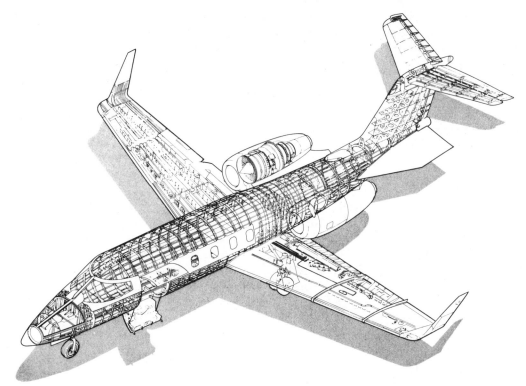

Cutaway view of Model 31 revealing structural, flight control, and propulsion system details. Learjet Corp.

The Model 31 wing has a 13-degree sweep and a span six feet wider than earlier Learjets. The wing was first used on the Model 28 Longhorn version and is very similar to that of the Model 55. The Model 31 wing also features the Century III wing modification's constant radius, high-lift leading edge.

Total fuel capacity of the Model 31 is 613 gallons, all contained in wing and fuselage tanks. A larger fuselage tank can be ordered to increase capacity to 686 gallons. To accommodate the aft tank, the aft pressure bulkhead is moved forward 14 inches, reducing the baggage compartment's size. As with other Learjets, the Model 31's engines are fed fuel by jet pumps. The fuselage tank uses gravity to drain fuel into the wing tanks and features an electric pump to transfer fuel if the gravity system fails.

The most unusual design features of the Model 31 are the two tail-mounted Delta Fins. The fins provide lift and a nose-down force only while flying at high angles of attack. The fins also increase the aircraft's directional stability at all speeds and improve its Dutch roll characteristics. They are particularly effective at low speeds and high angles of attack. In this scenario, the delta-shaped surfaces are positioned below the wake produced by the wing, providing lift in undisturbed air.

The lift the Delta Fins produce at the tail creates a nose-down pitching moment, making a stable "deep stall" impossible—even with full nose-up elevator at an extreme aft center of gravity position. This eliminates the need for the complex stall avoidance systems standard in preceding Learjets. It allows the full lift capability of the wing to be used. The end result is a reduced stall speed and shortened field length requirements.

The fins are aligned with the air flow during normal cruise conditions, so drag is minimal. As proof of this efficiency, the Model 31 is reported to have the lowest cruise fuel flow of any business jet, even those that cruise at significantly lower speeds.

Because of the Delta Fins and some other aerodynamic improvements, the Model 31 exhibits such docile yaw and Dutch roll damping characteristics that only a single yaw damper is installed. Unlike earlier models (which required dual yaw dampers), the yaw damper isn't required to dispatch the airplane. Elimination of these systems reduces weight, maintenance costs, and pilot workload. Single point refueling, which shortens the time required for turnaround and makes fueling tasks simpler, was later added as a standard feature on the Model 31.

The Learjet Corporation maintains that no other business jet in the world can operate from a 3,000-foot runway at maximum gross weight and climb directly to 47,000 feet. More specifically, the Model 31 can take off from a 2,966-foot runway with seven passengers and full fuel, climb directly to FL470 in just 28 minutes, and fly 1,500 nautical miles in 3 hours and 49 minutes. The Model 31 relies on the highly efficient wing, using a modified NACA Series 64A-109 airfoil, to achieve its high fuel efficiency standards.

Using the same basic TFE731-2 engine as the Model 35A, the Model 31's engine fuel controls have full redundancy. A new Digital Electronic Engine Control (DEEC) retains all previous conventional manual backups while increasing reliability with state-of-the-art electronic control technology. Specifically tailored for the Model 31, the new control has an improved idle power schedule to facilitate high altitude descent.

Certificated to operate at flight levels up to 51,000 feet, the Model 31 cruises routinely in the 45,000 to 51,000 feet range, well above the vast majority of air traffic and weather. These altitudes frequently permit ATC clearances directly to destinations.

The TTTS Competition

In 1988, Learjet Corporation, FlightSafety International, and Allied Signal Aerospace teamed to compete for the U.S. Air Force Tanker-Transport Training System (TTTS) program. FlightSafety was designated as prime contractor, responsible for development of all simulators, course materials, and training programs. Allied Signal was designated to supply the engines through its Garrett subsidiary and avionics from its Bendix-King subsidiary. The Air Force indicated that it wanted 14 simulators to train its pilots. Learjet Corporation was designated as a major subcontractor, proposing to supply a modified Model 31 together with necessary maintenance and logistics support. For its TTTS role, the Model 31's upper cockpit structure would be modified to accept two small "eyebrow" windows, which would improve visibility from the cockpit. A third crew seat for a cockpit instructor would be included. Cabin windows larger than those installed on standard Model 31s would be provided to improve visibility. A large airstair door would facilitate cabin entry.

The Air Force indicated its interest in buying up to 211 off-the-shelf business jets for the TTTS mission. In addition to Learjet, FlightSafety Services, and Allied Signal Aerospace, two other teams were competing for the contract, valued at a whopping $1.5 billion.

Modification of the Model 31 proposed by Learjet Corporation for the USAF Tanker Transport Training System (TTTS) competition. Learjet Corp.

Modular Design for Easy Servicing

The TFE731 engine is more complicated than a CJ610 because of the reduction gearing required to drive the fan assembly. Each major dynamic component of the engine comprises a modular section. Recognizing that the additional complexity could pose potential maintenance problems, Garrett introduced a new maintenance concept for business aircraft to hold down costs and minimize aircraft downtime. Most major sections of the TFE731 can be inspected in the field while the engine is in place on the airplane. If required, a single module can be removed from the engine and returned to a service facility, rather than removing the entire engine. Exchange modules are available to keep operator downtime to a minimum.

The bypass fan assembly module consists of a fan spinner, spinner support, fan rotor assembly, fan support assembly, planetary gear assembly, low-pressure compressor stator, bypass fan inlet housing, and fan bypass stator. The turbine section module includes a thrust nozzle and exhaust assembly, low-pressure turbine module, transmission duct, interstage temperature (ITT) thermocouple harness, combustion liner, high-pressure turbine wheel, and high-pressure turbine nozzle assembly.

Bypass Fan Assembly

A sound-attenuated inlet duct surrounds the geared bypass fan. The duct incorporates a ring of armor plate for fan blade containment in the unlikely event of a catastrophic fan failure. Airflow is discharged by the bypass fan into the bypass stator and low-pressure compressor (core) inlet stator. At sea level standard day conditions, airflow through the fan discharge duct is approximately 2.73 times higher than the airflow traveling through the engine core.

The forward end of the low-pressure (LP) spool drives a sun gear, which in turn drives five planetary gears. These planetary gears engage an outer ring gear to drive the bypass fan shaft. Fan speed, due to the planetary gear to sun gear reduction ratio of 1.8:1, is 11,483 rpm at 100% speed. A spinner covers the fan shaft forward end.

Low-Pressure (LP) Spool

The four-stage, axial-flow compressor wheels comprising the LP spool are mounted within the LP compressor housing on a drive shaft aligned through the use of curvic coupling teeth. Supporting the forward end of the shaft is a thrust-absorbing ball bearing to prevent oil flow into the compressor. At the shaft's aft end, a roller bearing provides support.

The LP compressor shaft extends to the rear of the engine where it fits, by way of curvic coupling teeth, with the forward end of the LP turbine shaft. The LP compressor and LP turbine shafts (which form the LP spool) are secured together by a tie bolt extending through the center of the HP drive shaft. During assembly, this bolt is stretched and secured with nuts at each end. This exerts restraining pressure against the shoulder at each end of the LP spool shaft, ensuring positive coupling teeth engagement. Use of curvic couplings also facilitates removal and replacement of low-pressure turbine components without affecting the stackup or curvic coupling engagement of the low-pressure compressor.

Each low-pressure compressor wheel has a nonrotating stator ring installed facing the compression flow. Each stator ring contains vanes that serve to direct airflow to the succeeding compressor wheel. The vanes also act as small diffuser ducts, causing air velocity to diminish slightly and pressure to increase.

As the airflow progresses through the four stages of compression, each successive compressor wheel and stator combination (called a stage) becomes smaller in size. This causes an increase of compressor air pressure as the airflow passes from stage to stage.

All nonrotating stator rings and low-pressure compressor shrouds are coated with an aluminum spray compound. During normal engine operation, this material becomes "machined" by wheel growth of the low-pressure compressor wheel blade tips. The result is a tight seal between the stator rings and low-pressure wheel tips.

A carbon face seal and rotor assembly is installed at the ball bearing on the forward end of the LP compressor drive shaft. The seal prevents lubrication oil from entering the compressor airstream. The carbon face seal is backed up by an air labyrinth seal.

Each axial flow turbine wheel has a nonrotating nozzle assembly at its entrance. These nozzles are similar to compressor stators in appearance but cause an opposite effect on gas flow; that is, gas flow velocity is increased (due to the nozzle's convergent design) as the gas stream approaches the turbine wheels. The nozzles are positioned to direct an optimum gas flow through the turbine wheel blades. Each turbine wheel is slightly larger in diameter than the preceding one to allow the gases to expand across the three stages of the low-pressure turbine.

The aft end of the low-pressure turbine shaft incorporates a carbon face seal and rotor assembly to prevent lubricating oil from entering the exhaust gas flow. This carbon face seal is also backed up by an air labyrinth seal.

High-Pressure (HP) Spool

A single high-pressure centrifugal compressor wheel, or impeller, is pressed onto the HP drive shaft at the forward end of the impeller. The aft end of the impeller incorporates curvic teeth to mesh with a curvic rotor seal that features two labyrinth air seals. The labyrinth seals are of the air-to-air type, designed to isolate high-pressure gases from regions of lower air pressure. The aft end curvic coupling engages the forward end of the HP turbine wheel so that the wheel is sandwiched between the curvic coupling and a rear coupling. All the components are forced together by a round nut that forces the two HP wheels and mating curvic couplings into the shaft shoulder located at the forward side of the centrifugal compressor.

A face shroud encloses the compressor impeller and directs all incoming airflow through the impeller blades. The shroud is bolted to the intermediate compressor housing, which also mounts the compressor diffuser. Airflow discharged from the HP impeller through its divergent-shaped diffuser expands into the combustor plenum. The plenum surrounds the combustion chamber assembly, functioning as a collector for compressor discharge air.

The HP axial flow turbine rotor receives the flow of high temperature gases from the combustion chamber. The gas flow is directed into the HP turbine through a sonic inlet HP turbine nozzle.

The HP turbine rotor shaft is supported at its forward end by a roller bearing and a thrust-absorbing ball bearing. Each bearing incorporates carbon oil seals. A bevel gear is mounted between the two bearings, being used to drive the accessory gear case through a radial tower shaft. The tower shaft protrudes through the engine housing at the six o-clock position. It is coupled to the transfer gear case.

Transfer Gear Case

The HP spool driving the bevel gear and tower shaft also couples to a bevel gear within the transfer gear case. A housed horizontal shaft, extending from the transfer gear case forward of and parallel to the centerline of the engine, drives gearing in the accessory gear case. The transfer gear case reduces input rpm from the HP spool shaft to 12,000 rpm maximum at the accessory gear drive shaft, resulting in a gear reduction ratio of about 2.5 to 1. In addition to transferring the HP shaft drive to the accessory case, the transfer gear case also mounts an N2 monopole pickup switch to sense HP rotor speed.

Accessory Gear Case

The accessory gear case is mounted along the bottom centerline of the TFE731 engine. Its gearing is driven by the horizontal shaft extending from the transfer gear case. Three mounting pads are provided at the forward side of the accessory gear case. The Learjet installation uses two of the pads to mount a starter-generator and hydraulic pump. The unused third pad can be used with installations on other aircraft to mount an alternator. The aft end of the accessory gear case incorporates mounting pads for driving the engine's fuel pump, fuel control, and oil pump pack. An oil filter, filter bypass, oil pressure regulator, and oil system breather pressurization valve are also mounted on the accessory gear case. At 100% rpm the starter-generator rotates at 12,000 rpm and the hydraulic pump at 6,000 rpm. All drive pads are equipped with lip-type oil seals, which may be removed readily and replaced if required.

Combustor

The basic function of the ring-shaped, annular combustor is to control the mixing of fuel and air. It contains the flame that heats the air flowing from the high-pressure compressor to the turbines. The annular reverse flow combustor contains 12 radial ports to accommodate duplex fuel atomizers. Additionally, two ports are provided to accommodate igniter plugs. The forward end of the combustor is lip-fitted into a transition duct. Its aft end is positioned and supported by hangar bolts extending through the turbine plenum.

Engine Bearing Identification

For purposes of identification, the low-pressure and high-pressure spool bearings are numbered as follows:

Bearing No. 1—Fan Shaft Forward Roller Bearing
Bearing No. 2—Fan Shaft Aft Ball Bearing
Bearing No. 3—LP Rotor Forward Ball Bearing
Bearing No. 4—HP Rotor Forward Roller Bearing
Bearing No. 5—HP Rotor Aft Ball Bearing
Bearing No. 6—LP Rotor Aft Roller Bearing

Bearings No. 1, 2, 3, and 6 are considered field replaceable, provided that the servicing technicians have adequate tooling and training. Bearings supporting the drive shafts in the transfer and accessory gear cases are not identified by any particular numerical system.

Surge Bleed Valve System

A characteristic of gas turbine engines is their tendency, under certain operating conditions, to stall or surge. Under a condition in which the flow of air from the compressor's inlet to its outlet is disturbed, surge can occur. Corresponding with each compressor rpm is a particular relationship between pressure increase and the volume of the compressor's airflow. Under some operating conditions this balance can become disturbed, and the result is compressor surge.

The surge bleed valve system, operated by the engine's electronic computer, is designed to avoid the surge range. It permits a certain portion of LP compressor air to bleed into the fan duct. Although this action implies that the compressor airflow is restricted during a surge condition, the opposite situation actually takes place. The restraint is reduced by opening a passage for air flow. The compressor is merely an air pump, and the air moving through the engine meets many obstacles to its flow. In particular, these include pressures within the combustor generated by the burning of fuel. If ''overfueling'' occurs, the pressure in the combustor may exceed the compressor discharge pressure. Should this occur, compressor discharge air cannot flow and the LP compressor tends to stall or surge.

During engine acceleration, when considerably more fuel is needed, combustor pressures are high, and stall and/or surge conditions are most apt to occur. An LP compressor stall condition may also occur when the HP compressor speed is lower than that of the LP compressor. In this case, LP airflow is discharged to the HP compressor. However, because the HP compressor is not performing its share of air pumping, a "stack-up" of air occurs at the HP compressor.

During engine acceleration the engine computer limits the maximum fuel flow. During deceleration of the engine, the computer prevents fuel flow from dropping below a minimum value. To accomplish these functions, the computer senses LP and HP speeds and controls fuel limits when there is a speed mismatch.

The computer also carefully controls surge bleed valve operation. The valve is closed as far as possible to maintain airflow energy to the turbine for fast acceleration characteristics. However, it must be open enough to permit unrestricted compressor airflow to avoid a stall or surge condition.

Anti-Ice System

The engine anti-ice system is comprised of a shutoff valve, pressure switch and solenoid. These components serve to control the flow of P3 compressor air to the engine anti-ice spinner. Air flow extraction from the compressor is limited to two percent of the total engine flow. Control of the anti-ice airflow is through a cockpit anti-ice switch, which must be placed in the "on" position by the pilot.

Engine Electrical System

All engine electrical components operate from the airplane's dc power source. Power to the engine computer itself is controlled by a cockpit on/off switch. When power is provided to the computer, it provides millivolt-level signals to a torque motor in the engine fuel control and to the surge bleed valve solenoids. The computer de-energizes a cockpit manual-mode annunciator light, signifying that the fuel system is in normal computer mode. If supply power or any of the input signals to the computer are interrupted, the cockpit manual-mode light will illuminate, indicating that the computer is off line.

Engine Fuel System Operation

Much like turbojet-powered airplanes, fanjet-powered Learjets use a fuel system having engine-driven pumps, which receive fuel at low-pressure from the fuel tanks and provide fuel to a nozzle. The fuel pressure rises between the engine pump and nozzle plumbing because of the nozzle's resistance. To overcome this resistance, the pressure must be relatively high. The nozzle and its atomizers break down the fuel into small droplets, vaporizing them to allow proper ignition and even burning.

The combustor is where burning of fuel and air takes place. An ignitor plug is used to light the fire. This provides all the basic components for lightoff; however, to accomplish the next objective—providing increasing fuel flow—some other key components must be added.

The engine-driven fuel pump is a positive displacement-type device having more capacity to pump fuel than is normally required by the engine. Therefore, metering and bypass valves are needed to control the amount of fuel actually reaching the atomizers. The bypass valve controls the amount of fuel being routed away from the metering valve. The two valves work as a team: when the metering valve closes, the bypass valve opens to bypass fuel back to the pump inlet. When the metering valve opens to provide more fuel for the engine, the bypass valve closes.

To maintain engine speed in response to the position of the cockpit power lever, a coordinator is needed. The coordinator senses power lever angle and other information, signaling the metering and bypass valves when to open and close. Coordination is normally provided by the electronic computer. When operating in the manual mode (due to computer failure), the metering valve changes its position in response to power lever angle, and the bypass valve is controlled by the effect of differential pressure across the metering valve. Finally, the system incorporates a shutoff valve and various monitors and controls.

Engine Fuel System Components

The TFE731 fuel system consists of a fuel pump assembly, hydromechanical fuel control, P3 limiter assembly, electronic computer, fuel flow divider assembly, and fuel nozzles. The fuel pump assembly is bolted to the accessory gear case on the aft left pad. The hydromechanical fuel control is mounted to the fuel pump assembly via a clamp for easy removal. The P3 limiter is an integral part of the fuel control but is considered a separate component. The flow divider assembly is bolted to the right side of the fuel control. The computer is isolated from the engine and is located within the airframe to protect it from temperature extremes. The 12 duplex fuel atomizers project radially through the turbine plenum into the combustor.

The fuel pump package houses a centrifugal low-pressure boost pump, a filter element, a filter-bypass valve and indicator to signal a stoppage, a temperature-controlled anti-ice valve, a vane-type high-pressure pump, and a high-pressure relief valve to regulate fuel pressure.

For Learjet applications (which use the -2B engine), the standard TFE731 anti-ice valve is removed and a motive-flow lockout valve and motive-flow pressure regulator are added in its place. On Learjet-configured engines, the fuel first flows through motive-flow devices. A motive-flow lock-out valve is constructed so that after a certain amount of fuel has passed through during starting, a pressure buildup will cause some of the fuel to be redirected. The pressure builds up because of the small orifice stroking the valve to the right against spring tension. This directs a portion of the fuel flow to the motive-flow pressure regulator. The regulator limits this fuel flow to 1,000 pounds per hour at 300 psi and directs it to the fuel jet pump. This pump, located at the bottom of the airplane's fuel tank, is unique in that it has no moving parts. Within the pump, the velocity of the fuel flow increases, owing to the converging orifice. As fuel leaves the orifice under pressure, it pulls in more fuel from the fuel tank. Acting as a boost pump, it then directs the fuel from the wing tank to the engine area where it enters the inlet side of the engine-driven boost pump to provide fuel needed for engine operation. Identical in operation to all jet pumps found on Learjet airplanes starting with the Model 23, this pump is used in preference to less reliable electrical boost pumps.

Electronic Fuel Metering

The heart of the TFE731's fuel system is a small electronic computer. Mounted remotely from the engine in the airframe, its primary function is to schedule the engine's fuel flow. Secondary functions include rapid-response protection against surge, overtemperature, and overspeed. Fuel flow schedules provided by the computer are similar to those of a typical hydromechanical fuel control. The only difference is that this fuel control uses electronic circuits to control the engine.

The computer requires the following engine inputs to perform its fuel flow scheduling functions: low-pressure spool (N1) rpm, high-pressure spool (N2) rpm, compressor inlet temperature (Tt2), compressor inlet pressure (Pt2), power lever angle (PLA), and interstage turbine temperature (ITT).

TFE731 Maintenance

The Garrett maintainability concept of the TFE731 allows considerable "on-wing" maintenance of the engine without removing it from the airplane. Because of its modular concept, the fan, fan gearbox, and low-pressure turbine modules can be removed from the installed engine. In addition, all but two stages of the low-pressure compressor can be visually inspected on an installed engine.

The TFE731 maintenance program uses a spectrographic oil analysis program (SOAP) check to provide a continuous indication of engine wear. SOAP involves taking an engine oil sample every 150 hours and sending it to the Garrett factory for analysis. By constantly tracking engine performance and foreign matter in the engine oil, preventative maintenance needs can be detected long before major costly repairs are required.

The Learjet 30 Series is also set up for the CAMP Systems, Inc. Maintenance Management Program. The Computerized Aircraft Maintenance Program (CAMP) eliminates the administrative burden involved in maintenance recordkeeping. It provides reports of the current maintenance status and history of the aircraft, engines, components, and accessories. The CAMP program also notes upcoming maintenance requirements based on either Learjet Corporation's recommended maintenance schedule or the operator's own program. Maintenance-due lists are accompanied by detailed procedures: estimated manhours, parts required, estimated parts costs, and special tools required. Learjet operators can get full access to their maintenance records from a desktop computer.

Combining the proven Learjet airframe with the benefits of fuel economy, low noise, and efficiency of fanjet power has kept the classic Learjet design current with today's technology. High-performance wing designs, winglets, and Delta Fins admirably distinguish the Learjet from its competitors, ensuring its presence at the world's airports well into the next century.

5

The 50 Series:
The Learjet Grows Up

Bill Lear had barely begun deliveries of the Model 24 when he started a full-blown design effort for a much larger executive jet transport. Designated the Model 40 Lear Liner, the ship would carry a maximum of 28 passengers and satisfy the market need for a jet positioned between the smaller Lear Jet and the McDonnell Douglas DC-9 or Boeing 737.

The Lear Liner would cruise at 508 miles per hour at 45,000 feet and feature a transcontinental range of 3,200 miles with 15 passengers aboard. Lear immersed himself in its design effort, and his engineers completed the detailed design of the Lear Liner during the summer of 1966. Construction of the first prototype was planned for the fall of that year. Typical of Lear's external optimism, he signed a $1 million contract with Rolls Royce for the Lear Liner's Spey-25 turbofan engines—before the first piece of metal for the new ship was cut. The same engine powered the BAC-111 jetliner in service with the airlines as well as the new Grumman Gulfstream II business jet.

Optimistically, Bill Lear promised to have the first Lear Liner in the air in 18 months, with the first delivery scheduled within a mere two years. Unfortunately, the Lear Liner never got off the ground—or even out of the shop, for that matter. Owing to the money crunch at Lear Jet Industries, another of Bill Lear's visions bit the dust.

The immediate prospects for the Lear Liner dimmed, but the vision stayed with Lear long after he left the company he had founded. Years after moving to Reno, Nevada, to pursue developments in steam engines and a variety of other entrepreneurial endeavors, he resurrected the idea of producing a "big" cabin executive airplane.

The LearStar 600 Emerges

Lear's new twin-turbofan jet transport was designated the LearStar 600. A new Nevada-based, privately owned company proposed to build the airplane. He made it clear that there would be no connection with Gates Learjet. At the time, Lear was also developing avionic and energy products for his Learavia and Lear Motors corporations at his Reno headquarters.

Engines selected for the LearStar 600 were 3,700-pound thrust TFE731-3 turbofans, growth versions of the Model 35 engines. The prototype airplane was to be built in Lear's hangar in Reno. Before setting out to develop an all-new design, Lear envisioned a complex retrofit program to modify existing Gates Learjet aircraft to improve their cruise range and landing and takeoff characteristics. The retrofit program called for designing a new wing that would make use of supercritical airfoil technology developed at the National Aeronautics and Space Administration's Langley Research Center. An outgrowth of these NASA investigations based on the Learjet design, Bill Lear did assessments of the LearStar 600 configuration through extensive wind tunnel testing. The combination of the NASA supercritical wing airfoil technology and a low drag area-rule, large-diameter fuselage would distinguish his new business jet entry.

Bill Lear sensed that the retrofit cost per airplane could exceed what Learjet owners would be willing to pay for it. After sampling the opinions of prospective customers, he was convinced to abandon the retrofit program and to develop a whole new airframe to take advantage of the supercritical wing's advanced performance characteristics. Lear also discovered that the market trend in new business jets was toward larger volume airplanes that provided walk-around comfort for passengers. The Learjet had proved itself as a business tool for primarily domestic flying; however, many operators were now contemplating transcontinental and transoceanic nonstop flight operations. The LearStar 600 would be designed for that growing market.

Preliminary LearStar 600 designs provided seating for 10 passengers. With a round outside fuselage diameter of 84 inches, the cabin would have a width of 80 inches and a maximum height of 75 inches. However, the spacious cabin dimensions could provide high density seating for up to 20 passengers. The supercritical wing planform used a 25-degree sweep, tailoring the airplane's lift/drag characteristics to allow flight planning for continuous, stepless climbs to cruise altitudes of 45,000 feet, where the LearStar 600 would cruise in the area of Mach 0.85 to 0.90. Lear considered cruise altitudes exceeding 45,000 feet but awaited the success of Gates Learjet's in-process program to certificate the Models 24 and 25 for cruising at 51,000 feet. He wanted to see what high-altitude FAA requirements would develop during the Gates Learjet program. Of particular interest were the structural and systems reliability design standards that might evolve.

Recognizing that neither he nor his business associates had access to the financial resources needed to manufacture the LearStar 600, Bill Lear sold the aircraft's exclusive production rights to Canadair, Inc. of Montreal, Canada, in April of 1976. The airplane was soon redesignated the CL-600 by that company. Still later, it was renamed the Challenger. Amply subsidized by the Canadian government, Canadair launched the production program on October 29, 1976, with 53 firm orders for the widebody business jet. Throughout its development, the Challenger suffered from a nagging overweight problem. Disgusted with the manner in which the Canadians revamped his lightweight, streamlined design, Bill Lear severed all ties with the project shortly after consummating the production license agreement. He would, however, be paid a royalty on each production Challenger sold.

Gates Introduces the 50 Series

On September 26, 1977, Gates Learjet marketing executives unveiled the Longhorn series, marking the occasion with the flight of a General Electric CJ610-powered Model

28 at Houston's Hobby Airport. It was the day before the opening of the National Business Aircraft Association (NBAA) annual meeting in that city. In addition to the 28, a longer-range variant, the Model 29, would be offered. This Learjet variant used a revolutionary wing incorporating winglets for enhanced fuel efficiency and uprated CJ610-8A engines for higher performance. The winglets were responsible for giving the ship its Longhorn name. The 28 and 29 models were the only available business jets capable of climbing directly to a 51,000 foot cruise altitude.

At the Paris Air Show in June of this same year, Gates Learjet released the first details of its new Model 50 Series. Prospective customers were told that the 50 Series would feature larger cabin dimensions than the 20 and 30 Series airplanes—the first "stand-up" cabin in the Learjet product line. It would be powered by a more powerful version of the TFE731 engine.

The larger Longhorn 50 Series was unveiled the next day with an exhibit of a full-scale cabin mockup. The 50 Series, comprised of the Models 54, 55, and 56, would carry the same distinctive winglets as the Models 28 and 29. With its modified wing, the 50 Series would have a 4-foot section added to each wingtip to accommodate mounting the NASA-developed winglets. The airplane would be larger than any other previous airplane in the Gates Learjet line.

The aerodynamic modifications that culminated in the 50 Series' new wing were first tested on August 24, 1977, using a prototype winglet-equipped wing fitted to a Model 25 fuselage. By reducing the induced drag of the wing, generated by the wingtip vortex, the Model 50 Series would offer more range (with the same fuel capacity) than it could without the winglets.

The 50 Series' larger diameter fuselage made it possible to mount the engines higher on the fuselage, lowering interference drag with the wing. As they had done with the earlier 30 Series models, Gates Learjet aerodynamists deleted the vortex generators from the wing's top surface, replacing them with boundary layer energizers to delay airflow separation over the wing. Two wing fences, components of the Gates Learjet Softflite modification proven on the 30 Series, were also added to each wing.

By April of 1978, construction of the prototype 50 Series airplane had begun in Wichita. Because of its size and complexity, completion of the prototype ship took the rest of that year. On February 2, 1979, the prototype rolled off the assembly line. Following more than two months of taxi tests and systems debugging, the ship completed its maiden flight on April 19. The prototype ship was a "generic" one. That is, it could later be deliverable as a Model 54, 55, or 56 ship. However, all variants featured the same winglets and Garrett TFE731-3 turbofan engines.

The 50 Series Certification Program

By 1980 Gates Learjet was successfully countering a trend in the general aviation industry characterized by sagging sales, discontinued product lines, and employee layoffs. Unlike many of its competitors, the company was hiring people, posting record sales levels—and pushing its 50 Series FAA certification program full speed ahead.

In March of that year, the company delivered its 1,000th Learjet, a Model 35A. It also rolled out the first production Model 55 from its new Tucson manufacturing facilities. The aircraft would be assembled in a newly built 196,000-square-foot assembly building dedicated to Model 50 production. This airplane, the third ship produced, was the first to be built in Tucson. The first two Model 55 prototypes were built in Wichita. The number one prototype was used primarily to prove the aircraft's flight characteristics and performance. The number two ship first flew in November 1979 and was used to evaluate the airplane's systems.

The two prototype Model 55s completed flutter tests that spanned the aircraft's entire performance envelope. Initially, only simple, easily solved problems were encountered. However, air separation, noise, and buffeting were encountered at 47,000 feet and at a 30-degree bank during the flutter tests. After installing wing tufts and using a chase aircraft to observe and photograph them, it was found that air separation was occurring on the fuselage above the wing and below the engine. Tufts are small lengths of yarn attached to the airframe to observe the direction of the airflow at the location of the tufts. The solution was to change the wing/fuselage fairing contour.

Milestones achieved during the test program included a single-engine climb to 29,000 feet with a takeoff weight of 20,560 pounds. The airplane also reached 37,000 feet in less than 20 minutes at a proposed certified maximum ramp weight of 19,750 pounds.

In spite of its larger size, the larger Model 55 features performance levels very similar to that of the Model 35A. Although Gates Learjet engineers conscientiously attempted to adhere to the specifications they developed in 1977 when the program was first announced, they were forced to downgrade some Model 55 performance projections as the airplane gradually increased in empty weight. Gates Learjet engineers had initially envisioned an 18,500-pound ramp weight with a 10,215-pound empty weight. The Model 55 was to have a balanced field length of 3,900 feet, capable of spanning a 2,585 nautical-mile range while carrying a 1,200 pound payload. By the time the aircraft first flew in 1979, the maximum takeoff weight had increased to 19,500 pounds, the empty weight was calculated at 10,992 pounds, and the balanced field length was estimated at 4,550 feet. The airplane's projected range had decreased about a hundred miles and was being pegged at 2,480 nautical miles.

These estimates were later modified to provide an empty weight of 11,255 pounds and a balanced field length of 4,715 feet. The range estimate was lowered to 2,406 nautical miles, with a corresponding reduction in fuel capacity of approximately 120 pounds. During 1980, Gates Learjet introduced an optional 20,500-pound maximum takeoff gross weight modification for the Model 55. It was made available to Gates Learjet customers at no additional cost.

A Design with Flexibility

Customer demand for the Model 50 had been excellent since the program's introduction at the 1977 NBAA show. With the growing number of orders, it was apparent that a second assembly line in Tucson would be needed almost immediately to satisfy the demand.

On March 18, 1981, the Model 55 received its FAR 25 type certificate, the culmination of the four-year development program. It was certificated for flight up to 51,000 feet and had the distinction of being the largest business jet produced by Gates Learjet Corporation.

On April 30, 1981, formal ceremonies were held in Tucson to deliver the first production Model 55 airplane (serial number 55-004) to a retail customer—Transcontinental

Gas Pipe Line Corporation of Houston, Texas. This Model 55 was the first Gates Learjet airplane completely built and finished at the company's Tucson facility. The delivery marked the 1,147th airplane leaving the factory since the company's original Model 23 went to the first customer in 1964.

Compared to earlier Learjets, the Model 55's cabin width was increased by 12 inches at the passenger shoulder height, with aisle headroom increased by 16 inches over predecessor model Learjets. Compared to 20 Series airplanes, cabin length was expanded by 6 feet 6 inches. This ''big'' Learjet could accommodate up to 11 passengers.

All three models of the 50 Series used the same basic fuselage, with identical external dimensions. However, the airplanes did vary in fuel capacity, range, and maximum take-off weight. The Model 54, certificated at 18,500 pounds, was projected to have a range of 2,424 miles and a fuel capacity of 867 U.S. gallons. The Model 55 had a range of 2,859 miles with a fuel capacity of 1,028 gallons at a gross weight of 19,500 pounds. The Model 56 featured a maximum takeoff weight of 20,500 pounds, making it capable of spanning a range of 3,468 miles on 1,236 U.S. gallons of fuel.

A spacious, luxurious cabin, featuring every amenity, pampers Model 55 passengers. Learjet Corp.

The Model 54 was not certificated due to a lack of sizable customer interest. While both 55 and 56 variants were certificated, only the Model 55 became a commercial success.

The powerplant for the 50 Series airplanes is the 3,700 pound thrust Garrett TFE731-3 turbofan. Its installation is similar to that on the Models 35 and 36, but the TFE731-3 differs from the TFE731-2 used in the 30 Series Learjets in several ways. To achieve the higher thrust rating (3,700 vs. 3,500 pounds), the engine operates at a modest increase in turbine inlet temperature of 85 degrees Fahrenheit. The engine incorporates an air-cooled, first stage high-pressure turbine. The -3 engine offers a slightly increased fan inlet total airflow, core airflow, and bypass ratio. It operates at a higher low-pressure rotor speed. Through a relocated pressure bleed-air port, the engine provides slightly more high-pressure bleed airflow for aircraft pressurization. Also the fan discharge duct has greater load carrying capability than the -2 engine. Finally, to structurally accommodate these upgrades, the engine weighs more. The TFE731-3 also has a smaller spinner and longer fan blades, which gives better high-altitude performance than the TFE731-2 delivers.

An electronic engine synchronizing system is standard and ensures minimum in-flight vibration levels. Single point refueling is offered as an option for the 50 Series airplanes, the first Learjets to offer this feature. Fuel heaters are an additional option.

The Model 55 incorporates engine thrust reversers as standard equipment. They are an effective way to augment the airplane's wheel braking system in reducing ground roll distance, brake wear, and tire wear. Each engine is equipped with a cascade-type thrust reverser, which is pneumatically operated and electrically controlled. A single control panel is mounted in the instrument panel's eyebrow area, containing an emergency stow switch and position annunciator lights for thrust reverser unlock, deploy, and bleed value. Arming, deployment, storage of the reversers, and engine rpm in the reverse thrust mode is controlled by piggyback levers mounted on the power levers. The reverser system provides full takeoff power in the reverse thrust mode at speeds down to about 60 knots. The reversers may be used to a full stop at idle thrust. The system weighs approximately 237 pounds.

In 1989, Learjet Corporation purchased the thrust reverser product line from Aeronca, which had previously built the units under contract to Learjet. Production of reversers was moved to Learjet's Wichita, facilities. In addition to use on the Model 55C, 35A, and 36A, Aeronca's thrust reversers are used on Falcon 20, Hawker DH-125-700, and Sabreliner 75A and 80 business jets.

The 50 Series airplanes incorporate a pressurization cycle that is designed to eliminate the pressurization bump felt on takeoff in older Learjets. A new Freon air conditioning system features dual evaporators for increased capability. Cockpit and cabin temperature levels can be controlled individually to suit crew and passenger preferences. Also, an old altitude limitation on operation of the airplane's Freon air conditioning compressor drive motor has been eliminated to allow air conditioning use at any altitude.

The 50 Series airplanes use engine compressor bleed air for wing anti-ice protection ("hot wing") and to de-fog the external windshield surface. The engine bleed system provides more flexibility than the 30 Series airplanes do at lower engine power settings because of the increased bleed airflow available from the TFE731-3 engine. Electrical power supplied by the airplane's dc power supply system is used to heat the tail surfaces.

The 50 Series flight control system is similar to that of the 30 Series. However, the 50 Series aircraft incorporate larger diameter cables and pulleys to reduce friction, and the autopilot is disconnected from the flight control system when it's not in use. The electrical pitch trim system has been upgraded to feature two speeds rather than the previous single speed.

Record-Setting Flights Follow Certification

On January 25, 1983, the Government of Canada followed the lead of other governments around the world and certificated the Model 55. Gates Learjet's newest and largest aircraft was now certificated and operating in eleven nations. The other countries included the United States, Spain, France, West Germany, Austria, Switzerland, Saudi Arabia, Australia, Venezuela, and Brazil. On March 9 of the same year, the FAA certificated the Model 55ER, the first in a planned series of extended-range versions of the 55. The 55ER featured a maximum range of 2,406 nautical miles with a standard 45-minute reserve. The first production Model 55ER was scheduled for customer delivery in July 1983.

On May 26, 1983, the FAA granted certification for the Model 55LR, still another variant of the Model 55. The 55LR differed from the standard 55 by having a maximum range of 2,608 nautical miles with the standard 45-minute fuel reserve. On the same day this variant was certificated, a 55LR established a new world speed record over a recognized course. It traveled from Los Angeles to Paris in a total elapsed time of 12 hours, 37 minutes, and 40 seconds, including a 19-minute fuel stop at Bangor, Maine. The 5,655-mile trip was flown at an average speed of 448.5 miles per hour. The airplane arrived at LeBourget Airport on the opening day of the 35th biennial Paris Air Show. On the return flight from Paris to Los Angeles on June 6th, the 55LR set a total elapsed time record of 14 hours, 36 minutes, and 42 seconds—which included a 17-minute, 40-second fuel stop at Halifax, Nova Scotia. Average speed on the return flight was 387.6 miles per hour. During the round trip, six separate world speed records were established.

Continuing to make record-setting headlines, a standard production Model 55 smashed six previous world records in the "time-to-climb" and "altitude" categories for business aircraft in its weight class during July of 1983. A Model 55 (serial number 55-052) departed Palm Springs, California, establishing new records at 3,000 meters (9,842.5 feet) in 2 minutes, 24 seconds; 6,000 meters (19,685 feet) in 4 minutes, 19 seconds; 9,000 meters (29,527.6 feet) in 6 minutes, 49 seconds; and 15,000 meters (49,212.5 feet) in 19 minutes, 25 seconds. The airplane reached its certificated operating altitude of 51,000 feet in 23 minutes, 57 seconds after takeoff.

On April 10, 1984, United Telecommunications of Kansas City took delivery of the 100th Model 55 to be manufactured by Gates Learjet. United Telecommunications already owned and operated two other Learjets. This Model 55 was the first Learjet equipped with the new GNS-1000 flight management system developed by Global Navigation Systems. It was also the first Model 55 to carry Collins Pro-Line II all-digital radios.

Model 55 Upgrades

On October 1, 1984, Gates Learjet unveiled an upgraded Model 55, featuring a 500-foot decrease in balanced field length at sea level and up to a 900-foot decrease when operating from high altitude runways. A 1,000-pound increase in maximum landing weight permitted more multi-leg missions without requiring refueling, offering a range increase of 36 percent and a full-fuel payload increase of up to 60 percent. On March 19, 1985, the FAA certified the Model 55 for a 10-passenger configuration, a 25-percent increase in capacity.

The new Model 55B made its formal debut at the 39th Annual National Business Aircraft Association meeting in Anaheim, California, on September 30, 1986. The original Model 55 had evolved into the 55B, incorporating a fully integrated Collins all-digital avionics and autopilot package as standard equipment. In addition to this variant's high-tech cockpit, the 55B boasts increased range, a higher useful load, and expanded mission flexibility.

The Collins avionics package features an all-digital dual channel autopilot, an advanced attitude heading reference system (AHRS), digital air data system, and an electronic flight instrument system (EFIS). Each element of the system is interconnected via a digital multiplex bus, reducing the weight of aircraft wiring harnesses and minimizing maintenance requirements.

The 55B features simplified system mode switching. Heading and course controls are located on the cockpit's center console, with autopilot controls on the center glareshield. An emergency bus switch directs battery power to essential systems if normal power sources are disrupted.

As an option, a Gemini auxiliary power unit (APU), manufactured by Sundstrand Turbomach of San Diego, California, first became available on the 55B. The APU, a small self-contained gas turbine, provides electrical power to operate all aircraft systems, including the 55B's Freon air conditioning system on the ground. The APU can also be used for main engine starting, in lieu of using the on-board ship's batteries or a ground power unit. The APU is certified for both ground operation and in-flight use to approximately 20,000 feet as an emergency power source. Compact and lightweight, the APU is installed in the tailcone area of the aircraft and does not affect the 55B's baggage carrying capacity.

On September 29, 1987, the Model 55C was introduced at the 40th National Business Aircraft Association annual meeting in New Orleans. The 55C, considered by a number of industry observers to be the best overall performer of any medium jet, is a further refinement of the 50 Series aircraft. It features Delta Fins, which are fixed aerodynamic surfaces mounted on the sides of the lower rear fuselage to provide superior handling characteristics at slower speeds; that is, the airplane stalls at a lower airspeed, significantly reducing balanced field length and enabling the 55C to operate from relatively short runways.

The 55C's Unique Aerodynamic Enhancements

The Delta Fins featured on the 55C eliminate the possibility, and danger, of horizontal stabilizer-blanketing, which could otherwise occur during "deep" stalls. The fins prevent this condition by pushing the Model 55C's nose downward, facilitating recovery from the stall. The large fins are mounted under the tailcone, forming an inverted V shape. With highly swept leading edges, they generate little lift or drag in normal cruise; but when the airplane operates at a high angle of attack, the fins produce lift to force the

Powerful Model 55C climbs above the cumulus. Learjet Corp.

nose back down. At a stalling attitude, the fins fly in unobstructed air. The lift they produce assures that the 55C cannot enter a deep stall condition, even if the T-tail is blanketed by the wing wake.

The Model 55C's Delta Fins augment the airplane's handling characteristics in two important ways. First, Dutch roll is sufficiently dampened to eliminate a requirement for the second yaw damper needed on other Learjets to provide an adequate level of directional stability. The 55C autopilot functions as the primary backup to the single Collins yaw damper. An unusually large performance envelope, not requiring yaw damper operation, is the secondary backup. The Model 55C has been proven to have excellent flight characteristics with the yaw damper inoperative. Although the nine-foot-long Delta Fins do add some weight and drag, this is compensated for by the reduction in weight created by elimination of the aircraft's stick-pusher system and the second yaw damper. New engine pylons also help to offset much of the Delta Fin's drag.

During later flight testing of the 55C variant, Learjet test pilots were amazed to note that the airplane flew more efficiently with tufts installed on the wings. Apparently the tufts changed the boundary layer of the airflow over the wing's surface. The result was improved performance and stall behavior. In the production Model 55C, round-head machine screws were substituted for some of the smooth, flush-head ones that attach the leading edge to the wing structure. Round-head screws emulate the action of the tufts—they make the Model 55C fly more efficiently.

Avionics That Rival Any

The Model 55C uses a similar power generation scheme to that of all predecessor Learjets from the Model 23 onward, with engine-driven starter-generators for primary dc power, dc to ac inverters for secondary ac power and the aircraft batteries for emergency power. However, a number of refinements in the 55C's electrical system offer additional safety provisions.

Lead acid batteries, rather than nickel cadmium (ni-cad) ones, provide power for engine starting and primary emergency power. They provide an additional margin of safety by eliminating potential thermal runaway problems associated with ni-cad batteries. Also, the need for additional ni-cad temperature monitoring instrumentation is unnecessary. The 55C features a dc and ac emergency electrical power and distribution system. It is comprised of a tailcone-mounted current limiter box and relay, an easily accessible cockpit mounted switch, relays in each circuit breaker panel, and a third dc to ac inverter colocated with a second emergency battery. The 55C's emergency bus system provides load shedding of nonessential electrical loads during emergency conditions. When this emergency bus is activated, battery power is removed from a battery charging bus and those loads connected to the emergency bus are powered directly from the aircraft batteries. All loads, except the systems tied to the emergency bus, a hot battery bus, and standby batteries, are dropped off the line.

To ensure that a total electrical failure will never occur in a 55C, the airplane is equipped with two Jet Electronics & Technologies, Inc. (J.E.T.) PS-835 emergency batteries. One of these battery packs contains a dc to ac converter. The converter receives power from the battery, converting it to a lower voltage for instrument internal lighting. Connected to the second standby battery is a 75 VA J.E.T. dc to ac inverter. This inverter supplies single phase, 115 Vac, 400 Hz power to the emergency ac bus system. This 115 Vac power is also supplied to an autotransformer, located in the copilot's circuit breaker panel, for supplying 26 Vac power to other critical devices during emergency bus operation. An emergency bus current limiter fuse box, mounted in the 55C's tailcone, contains two 40-amp current limiters to protect the emergency bus feeder cables.

The pilot's communication and navigation radios, together with audio intercommunications, are powered from the 55C's essential bus(s) during normal operation, and when the airplane's emergency bus is selected they are transferred to it. Position of the aircraft's avionic master switch remains unchanged regardless of the bus from which the power is derived. Electrical power is supplied by either the 55C's batteries (emergency bus) or the emergency power supplies. Fully charged batteries should be capable of powering the minimum electrical equipment for night instrument flight for approximately 2.5 hours.

The Model 55C offers one of the most advanced avionics packages available in any business jet. The standard package includes a fully integrated, all-digital electronic flight instrument system (EFIS). Digital electronics offer better reliability, quicker response, smaller components, lighter weight, and reduced operating costs compared to their analog counterparts. A Collins EFIS-85 System, combined with a Collins APS-85 automatic flight control system, a pilot's and copilot's flight director system, and weather radar, provide 55C pilots with many flight control system features not found in conventional instrument systems.

Model 55C features an "all-digital" cockpit with electronic flight instruments. Learjet Corp.

As on the advanced flight decks of the Boeing 757 and 767, cathode ray tubes (CRTs) replace a number of conventional analog flight instruments. Warning lights and annunciators formerly scattered throughout the cockpit are integrated into the CRT displays. By eliminating hundreds of moving mechanical parts, reliability is increased dramatically in a so-called "glass cockpit." Using high-efficiency phosphors, CRT displays offer high visual contrast, brightness, and resolution to allow accurate reading even during bright sunlight conditions.

The Collins five-tube EFIS-85 system consists of four identical EFD-85 electronic flight display units (CRT displays) for displaying flight information. Two DCP-85E display processor control panels are provided to enable the crew to select various operating modes. Using the two CHP-86D course heading panels, the crew selects the desired aircraft heading and course. An MPU-85 multifunction processor unit and an MFD-85 multifunction display (which is driven by the MPU-85) provide the crew with a systems information window. Rounding out the integrated system, two reversionary mode panels provide system operational capabilities in the event of a system failure.

The electronic attitude director indicator (EADI) display provides an amazing array of flight information to the crew: pitch and roll attitude, steering commands, glideslope deviation, localizer deviation, autopilot annunciation, speed deviation, radio altitude, decision height, marker beacon annunciation, flight guidance mode annunciation, V-bar or cross pointer commands, reversionary composite mode, go-around annunciation, marker beacon display, comparator warning, inclinometer, LRN annunciation, speed with trend monitor, and altitude information.

A companion electronic horizontal situation indicator (EHSI) has three modes of operation. The modes are selectable through the DCP-85E display control panel. The first mode is a full compass rose mode, which selects a display very similar to a conventional electromechanical horizontal situation indicator (HSI) presentation. Included are digital readouts of distance, elapsed time, time-to-go, ground speed, wind, and selected course. A VOR, ADF, or LRN bearing pointer can also be displayed.

The second mode is an expanded compass sector. In this mode, a section of the compass card is located across the top of the display with an airplane symbol located at the bottom center. Weather radar information may also be displayed in this mode.

The third mode provides the same display as the second mode except that the course pointer and deviation bar are replaced by active course lines to the selected VORTAC or waypoint symbols.

The EHSI also displays an incredible amount of information: true/magnetic heading, selected heading, selected course, preselected course, lateral deviation from preselected course, radar target alert, digital readout of selected course, time to station/waypoint, source labels for preset course, source label for bearing point, numerous flags, navigation data source annunciation, lateral deviation from selected course, to/from, distance to station/waypoint, ground speed, bearing pointer (VOR, ADF, etc.), glideslope deviation, and angular/linear deviation annunciation.

Because the Model 55's increased cabin size provides a new level of crew and passenger comfort during longer flights, some operators purchase the Model 55 specifically for international travel. As a result, the 55C's avionics sophistication has reached a new high for the Learjet series. Specifically, many long-range navigation systems are installed. Manufacturers of these systems include Collins, Global Navigation Systems, and Litton VLF/Omega. Few of the far more expensive inertial navigation systems (INS) have found their way into Learjets, being reserved mainly for aircraft in the category of Boeing 747s, 767s, and Gulfstream IVs.

Because the Model 55C can comfortably span the world's oceans, the need for an accurate long-range navigation aid became a strict requirement for such travel. The VLF/Omega navigation system uses the worldwide stations established by the U.S. Navy and U.S. Coast Guard. Presently, there are less than 20 of these stations in the entire free world. However, the locations of the stations and the fact that they use very low frequency (VLF) signals ranging from 10 to 30 kHz results in global coverage. Equipped with an Omega system, a Learjet can use the signals to navigate anywhere on the face of the earth.

Even a Cockpit Voice Recorder

Since 1958, all large passenger-carrying airliners flying in the United States have been required by FAA regulation to be equipped with an automatic flight data recording system. The system monitors both flight parameters and cockpit conversations. Just like the latest commercial jet airline transports, the Model 55C can be equipped with an optional cockpit voice recorder to aid in post-crash accident investigations.

The Fairchild A100A Cockpit Voice Recorder (CVR) is an endless magnetic tape device that records all voice signals transmitted or received by 55C pilots for a maximum period of 30 minutes of continuous operation; voice recordings beyond 30 minutes of continuous operation are automatically erased. The recorder is housed in an international orange, one-half ATR short equipment case. It has a magnetic tape recorder assembly with a radio locator beacon and control unit assembly. The CVR is enclosed in a crushproof case mounted in the Model 55C's tailcone. The tape unit is fire-resistant and contains a radio transmitter beacon to help accident rescue crews locate the unit underwater.

Learjet assembly line showing fitting of detail airframe parts prior to installation of aircraft systems. Learjet Corp.

Learjet: No End in Sight

At the close of the 1980s, Learjet Corporation was continuing to concentrate its marketing efforts on the 31 and the 55C as well as the 35/36 series. All these airplanes exemplify an advanced refinement of Bill Lear's original design for the Model 23. During the span of a quarter-century, major technological advances in turbine engines, aerodynamics, and avionic systems contributed to the aircraft's remarkable performance and popularity. New management seeks to keep the company profitable by resisting overexpansion and building a limited number of virtually custom-built Learjets each year. There is every reason to believe that the Learjet Corporation will continue to prosper, successfully selling both its existing and future new-technology business aircraft well into the next century.

6
Specifications and Performance

All models of the Learjet product line are built of conventional aluminum alloy, semi-monocoque construction. The rugged Learjet wing uses an eight-spar construction with either tiptanks or winglets. Many different configurations of wings have been used over the years: tiptanks, vortex generators, winglets, and boundary layer devices. The aircraft's empennage consists of an all-flying T-type horizontal stabilizer. The undercarriage is a hydraulically retractable tricycle type featuring anti-skid braking and electrically operated nosewheel steering.

The primary flight controls on all Learjets consist of manually actuated control surfaces. The aircraft's flaps and spoilers are hydraulically actuated. An electrically actuated aileron, rudder, and pitch trim system is standard on all variants of the airplane. For cabin pressurization, engine bleed air is used, typically maintaining a 9.4 psi cabin pressure differential. The Learjet fuel systems are all similar, with gravity feed from wing and fuselage tanks supplemented by jet pumps. The configuration of all Learjet electrical systems is basically the same. The 28 Vdc primary system is powered by two starter-generators, two nickel-cadmium or lead-acid batteries. Later Learjet variants feature system safety enhancements, including emergency buses and standby battery packs for uninterrupted power in the unlikely event of total inflight power failure. For powering avionics and instruments, a 115-volt ac secondary system with two or three inverters is installed. Hydraulic systems are typically comprised of two engine-driven pumps, supplemented by an electrically driven auxiliary pump and accumulator.

Model 23 Specifications and Performance

Certification: CAR Part 23 Normal Category
Minimum crew: pilot and copilot
Passenger capacity: up to seven
Powerplant: two each General Electric CJ610-4 turbojets
Takeoff thrust: 2,850 lb. thrust each

Wing span: 35 ft. 7 in.
Length: 43 ft. 3 in.
Height: 12 ft. 7 in.
Wing area: 231 sq. ft.

Empty weight: 6,150 lb.
Maximum takeoff weight: 12,500 lb.
Maximum speed: 561 mph at 24,000 ft.
Economy cruising speed: 485 mph at 40,000 ft.
Service ceiling: 45,000 ft.
Range with max. fuel at economy cruising speed: 1,830 miles

Learjet 24 Specifications and Performance

Certification: CAR 4b Transport Category
Minimum flight crew: pilot & copilot
Passenger capacity: up to six
Powerplant: two each General Electric CJ610-8A turbojets
Takeoff thrust: 2,950 lb. thrust each

Wing span: 35 ft. 7 in.
Length: 43 ft. 3 in.
Height: 12 ft. 3 in.
Wing area: 231.77 sq. ft.

Empty weight: 7,064 lb.
Maximum takeoff weight: 13,500 lb.

Maximum speed: 547 mph @ 25,000 ft.
Economy cruising speed: 493 mph @ 47,000 ft.
Service ceiling: 51,000 ft.
Range with 4 passengers, max. fuel plus 45 min. reserve: 1,830 miles

Learjet 25D Specifications and Performance

Certification: FAR Part 25 Transport Category
Approved operations: day, night, VFR, IFR, & flight into known icing conditions
Minimum flight crew: pilot & copilot
Passenger seating capacity: up to eight
Powerplant: two each General Electric CJ610-8A turbojet with thrust reversers
Takeoff thrust: 2,950 lb. each static thrust at sea level
Engine time-between-overhaul (TBO): 5,000 hrs.

Length: 47 ft. 7 in.
Height: 12 ft. 3 in.
Wing span: 35 ft. 7 in.
Wing area: 231.8 sq. ft.
Main wheel treat: 8 ft. 3 in.

Wheel base: 19 ft. 2 in.
Cabin length: 16 ft. 3 in.
Cabin height: 52 in.
Cabin width: 59 in.
Baggage volume: 40 cu. ft.
Entry door size: 24 × 62 in.

Empty weight: 8,121 lb.
Maximum ramp weight: 15,500 lb.
Payload with full fuel: 881 lb.
Maximum takeoff weight: 15,000 lb.
Maximum landing weight: 13,300 lb.

FAR 25 balanced field length: 3,937 ft.
Two engine rate of climb @ takeoff: 6,830 fpm
Single engine rate of climb @ takeoff: 1,910 fpm
Engine out service ceiling: 23,500 ft.
Cruise speed: 528 mph @ 41,000 ft.
Maximum operating speed: 0.81 Mach above 24,000 ft.
Maximum range: 1,579 statute miles
Maximum certified ceiling: 51,000 ft.
Landing approach speed: 143 mph IAS
Stall speed (landing configuration): 112 mph IAS
FAR 91 landing distance: 2,817 ft.
FAR 36 noise level on takeoff: 90.1 EPNdb

Learjet 25D Economics (Direct Operating Cost)

Fuel (245 GPH @ $1.65/gal): $404.25 per hour
Maintenance labor: $92.93 per hour
Maintenance material: $66.55 per hour
Engine accrual for overhaul: $93.80 per hour
Miscellaneous (oil, crew travel, landing, parking, cabin supplies): $34.00 per hour
Total costs per hour: $691.53
Block speed (including taxi/takeoff): 426 mph
Direct cost per mile: $1.62

Learjet 25G Specifications And Performance

Certification: FAR Part 25 Transport Category
Approved operations: day, night, VFR, IFR, & flight into known icing conditions
Minimum flight crew: pilot & copilot
Passenger seating capacity: up to eight
Powerplant: two each General Electric CJ610-8A turbojet with thrust reversers
Takeoff thrust: 2,950 lb. each static thrust @ sea level
Engine time-between-overhaul (TBO): 5,000 hrs.

Length: 47 ft. 7 in.
Height: 12 ft. 3 in.
Wing span: 35 ft. 7 in.
Wing area: 246.8 sq. ft.
Main wheel tread: 8 ft. 3 in.
Wheel base: 19 ft. 2 in.
Cabin length: 16 ft. 3 in.
Cabin height: 52 in.
Cabin width: 59 in.
Baggage volume: 40 cu. ft.
Entry door size: 24 × 62 in.

Empty weight: 8,250 lb.
Maximum ramp weight: 16,800 lb.
Payload with full fuel: 1,556 lb.
Maximum takeoff weight: 16,300 lb.
Maximum landing weight: 13,700 lb.

FAR 25 balanced field length: 5,148 ft.
Cruise speed: 534 mph @ 41,000 ft.
Maximum operating speed: 0.81 Mach above 24,000 ft.
Maximum range: 2,070 statute miles
Maximum certified ceiling: 51,000 ft.
FAR 91 landing distance: 2,690 ft.
FAR 36 noise level on takeoff: 90.1 EPNdb

Learjet 25G Economics (Direct Operating Cost)

Fuel (224 GPH @ $1.65/gal): $369.60 per hour
Maintenance labor: $92.93 per hour
Maintenance material: $66.55 per hour
Engine accrual for overhaul: $93.80 per hour
Miscellaneous (oil, crew travel, landing, parking, cabin supplies): $34.00 per hour
Total costs per hour: $656.88
Block speed (including taxi/takeoff): 437 mph
Direct cost per mile: $1.50

Learjet 28/29 Specifications and Performance

Certification: FAR Part 25 Transport Category
Approved operations: day, night, VFR, IFR & flight into known icing conditions
Minimum flight crew: pilot & copilot
Passenger seating capacity: up to ten (28) or eight (29)
Powerplant: two each General Electric CJ610-8A turbojet with thrust reversers
Takeoff thrust: 2,950 lb. each static thrust at sea level
Engine time-between-overhaul (TBO): 5,000 hrs.

Length: 47 ft. 9 in.
Height: 12 ft. 1 in.
Wing span: 43 ft. 8 in.
Wing area: 264.5 sq. ft.
Main wheel tread: 8 ft. 3 in.
Cabin length: 14 ft. 8 in. (28) or 12 ft. 8 in. (29)
Cabin height: 52 in.
Cabin width: 59 in.

Empty weight: 8,568 lb. (28) or 8,524 lb. (29)
Maximum ramp weight: 15,500 lb.
Payload with full fuel: 1,848 lb.
Maximum takeoff weight: 15,000 lb.
Maximum landing weight: 14,300 lb.

FAR 25 balanced field length: 2,998 ft.
Two engine rate of climb @ takeoff: 6,950 fpm
Cruise speed: 534 mph
Maximum operating speed: 0.82 Mach above 24,000 ft.
Landing approach speed: 119 KIAS
Stall speed (landing configuration): 89 KIAS
FAR 91 landing distance: 2,734 ft.
FAR 36 noise level on takeoff: 94.0 EPNdb

Learjet 28/29 Economics (Direct Operating Cost)

Fuel (233 GPH @ $1.65/gal): $384.45 per hour
Maintenance labor: $92.93 per hour
Maintenance material: $66.55 per hour
Engine accrual for overhaul: $93.80 per hour
Miscellaneous (oil, crew travel, landing, parking, cabin supplies): $34.00 per hour
Total costs per hour: $671.73
Block speed (including taxi/takeoff): 416 mph
Direct cost per mile: $1.62

General Electric CJ610-8A Turbojet Engine

Compressor type: axial flow eight-stage
Turbine type: two-stage reaction turbine
Compressor anti-icing: bleed air circulated through inlet guide vanes
Pressure ratio: 6.3
Air flow (pound/sec): 44.0
RPM: 16,700 (limit)
Length: 45.4 in.
Maximum diameter: 17.7 in.
Weight: 411 lb.
Fuel control: hydromechanical

Takeoff thrust (sea level, standard day): 2,950 lb.
Specific fuel consumption (SFC): 0.97
Maximum continuous thrust (sea level): 2,850 lb.
Specific fuel consumption: 0.97
Maximum cruise thrust (.8M/36K): 890 lb.
Specific fuel consumption: 1.14
Thrust-to-weight ratio: 7.2 to 1

Learjet 35A/36A Specifications and Performance

Certification: FAR Part 25 Transport Category
Approved operations: day, night, VFR, IFR, & flight into known icing conditions
Minimum flight crew: pilot & copilot
Passenger seating capacity: up to eight (35A) or six (36A)
Powerplant: two each Garrett TFE 731-2-2B turbofan with thrust reversers
Takeoff thrust: 3,500 lb. each static thrust at sea level
Engine time-between-overhaul (TBO): progressive maintenance

Length: 48 ft. 8 in.
Height: 12 ft. 3 in.
Wing span: 39 ft. 6 in.
Wing area: 253.3 sq. ft.
Main wheel tread: 8 ft. 3 in.
Wheel base: 20 ft. 2 in.
Cabin length: 21 ft. 9 in. (35A) or 18 ft. 0 in. (36A)
Cabin height: 52 in.
Cabin width: 59 in.
Baggage volume: 40 cu. ft. (35A) or 27 cu. ft. (36A)
Entry door size: 24 × 62 in.

Empty weight: 9,838 lb.
Maximum ramp weight: 18,500 lb.
Payload with full fuel: 2,064 lb. (35A) or 862 lb. (36A)
Maximum takeoff weight: 18,300 lb.
Maximum landing weight: 15,300 lb.

FAR 25 balanced field length: 4,972 ft.
Two engine rate of climb @ takeoff: 4,340 fpm
Single engine rate of climb @ takeoff: 1,280 fpm
Engine out service ceiling: 25,000 ft.
Cruise speed: 529 mph @ 41,000 ft.
Maximum operating speed: 0.81 Mach above 24,000 ft.
Maximum range: 2,567 statute miles (35A) or 3,051 statute miles (36A)
Maximum certified ceiling: 45,000 ft.
Landing approach speed: 147 mph IAS
Stall speed (landing configuration): 112 mph IAS
FAR 91 landing distance: 3,075 ft.
FAR 36 noise level on takeoff: 83.9 EPNdb

Learjet 35A/36A Economics (Direct Operating Cost)

Fuel (172 GPH @ $1.65/gal): $283.80 per hour
Maintenance labor: $101.15 per hour
Maintenance material: $78.48 per hour
Engine accrual for overhaul: $140.14 per hour
Miscellaneous (oil, crew travel, landing, parking, cabin supplies): $34.00 per hour
Total costs per hour: $637.57
Block speed (including taxi/takeoff): 426 mph
Direct cost per mile: $1.50

Learjet 31 Specifications and Performance

Certification: FAR Part 25 Transport Category
Approved operations: day, night, VFR, IFR & flight into known icing conditions
Minimum flight crew: pilot & copilot
Passenger seating capacity: up to 10
Powerplant: two each Garrett TFE 731-2-3B turbofan with thrust reversers
Takeoff thrust: 3,500 lb. each static thrust at sea level

Length: 48 ft. 8 in.
Height: 12 ft. 3 in.
Wing span: 43 ft. 9 in.
Wing area: 264.5 sq. ft.
Main wheel tread: 8 ft. 3 in.
Wheel base: 20 ft. 2 in.
Cabin length: 21 ft. 9 in.
Cabin height: 52 in.
Cabin width: 59 in.
Baggage volume: 40 cu. ft.
Cabin entry door size: 24 × 62 in.

Empty weight: 9,857 lb.
Zero fuel weight: 12,600 lb.
Maximum ramp weight: 15,750 lb.
Payload with full fuel: 1,383 lb.
Maximum takeoff weight: 15,500 lb.
Maximum landing weight: 15,300 lb.

FAR 25 balanced field length: 2,966 ft.
Two engine rate of climb @ takeoff: 5,480 fpm
Single engine rate of climb @ takeoff: 1,890 fpm
Engine out service ceiling: 31,200 ft.
Cruise speed: 514 mph @ 43,000 ft.
Maximum operating speed: 0.78 Mach above 29,000 ft.
Maximum range: 1,875 statute miles
Maximum certified ceiling: 51,000 ft.
Landing approach speed: 139 mph IAS

Stall speed (landing configuration): 107 mph IAS
FAR 91 landing distance: 3,010 ft.
FAR 36 noise level on takeoff: 83.0 EPNdb

Learjet 31 Economics (Direct Operating Cost)

Fuel (150 GPH @ $1.65/gal): $247.50 per hour
Maintenance labor: $99.80 per hour
Maintenance material: $78.48 per hour
Engine accrual for overhaul: $140.14 per hour
Miscellaneous (oil, crew travel, landing, parking, cabin supplies): $34.00 per hour
Total costs per hour: $599.92
Block speed (including taxi/takeoff): 414 mph
Direct cost per mile: $1.45

TFE731 Turbofan Specifications and Performance

Type: two-spool turbofan with reverse-flow annular combustor
Low-pressure spool: four-stage axial flow compressor/three stage turbine
High-pressure spool: single-stage centrifugal compressor/single-stage turbine
Fuel control: hydromechanical augmented with electronic computer
Absolute maximum operating altitude: 45,000 ft.
Rated takeoff thrust: 3,500 lbs. up to 72° F. at sea level
Thrust specific fuel consumption (TSFC): 0.504 PPH/lb. thrust (-2B engine)
Oil system capacity: approximately 12.0 quarts
Engine starting power required: 28 Vdc, 500 amp (1,000 amp inrush)

Learjet 55C Specifications and Performance

Certification: FAR Part 25 Transport Category
Approved operations: day, night, VFR, IFR, & flight into known icing conditions
Minimum flight crew: pilot & copilot
Passenger seating capacity: up to 10
Powerplant: two each Garrett TFE 731-3AR-2B turbofan with thrust reversers
Takeoff thrust: 3,700 lb. each static thrust at sea level
Engine time-between-overhaul (TBO): progressive maintenance

Length: 55 ft. 1 in.
Height: 14 ft. 8 in.
Wing span: 43 ft. 9 in.
Wing area: 264.5 sq. ft.
Main wheel tread: 8 ft. 3 in.
Wheel base: 23 ft.
Cabin length: 22 ft.
Cabin height: 68.5 in.
Cabin width: 70.8 in.
Baggage volume: 57.5 cu. ft.
Cabin entry door size: 24 × 67 in.

Empty weight: 12,622 lb.
Maximum zero fuel weight: 15,000 lb.
Maximum ramp weight: 21,250 lb.
Payload with full fuel: 1,538 lb.
Maximum takeoff weight: 21,000 lb.
Maximum landing weight: 18,000 lb.

FAR 25 balanced field length: 5,039 ft.
Two engine rate of climb @ takeoff: 4,176 fpm
Single engine rate of climb @ takeoff: 1,240 fpm
Cruise speed: 523 mph @ 41,000 ft.
Maximum operating speed: 0.79 Mach above 45,000 ft.
Maximum range: 2,556 statute miles
Maximum certified ceiling: 51,000 ft.
Landing approach speed: 157 mph IAS
Stall speed (landing configuration): 122 mph IAS
FAR 91 landing distance: 3,250 ft.
FAR 36 noise level on takeoff: 86.3 EPNdb

Learjet 55C Economics (Direct Operating Cost)

Fuel (174 GPH @ $1.65/gal): $287.10 per hour
Maintenance labor: $104.86 per hour
Maintenance material: $89.36 per hour
Engine accrual for overhaul: $147.88 per hour
Miscellaneous (oil, crew travel, landing, parking, cabin supplies): $34.00 per hour
Total costs per hour: $663.20
Block speed (including taxi/takeoff): 421 mph
Direct cost per mile: $1.58

Appendix: Chronology of Major Learjet Events

February 2, 1963—Assembly of Learjet #1 begins.

June 7, 1963—First fuselage leaves its jigs.

August 2, 1963—Forward and aft fuselage sections are mated.

August 16, 1963—Wings and fuselage are mated.

September 15, 1963—Rollout of #1 Learjet.

October 7, 1963—First flight of first Model 23.

March 5, 1964—First flight of second Model 23.

April 1, 1964—FAA certification for Model 23 begins.

May 15, 1964—First flight of third Model 23.

July 30, 1964—Lear Jet Corporation applies to SEC to issue stock to public.

July 31, 1964—Model 23 awarded FAA type certificate.

October 13, 1964—First production Model 23, the third aircraft off the assembly line, is delivered to Chemical and Industrial Corporation of Cincinnati.

November 30, 1964—Lear Jet Corporation becomes publicly owned.

February 19, 1965—Lear Jet Stereo operation is relocated to Detroit, Michigan.

May 21, 1965—Model 23 establishes three official world speed records in a "dawn to dusk" transcontinental flight from Los Angeles to New York City and back.

October 21, 1965—First fatal Learjet accident in Michigan.

November 14, 1965—Second fatal Learjet crash occurs in California.

December 14, 1965—A standard, production line Model 23 flies to 40,000 feet in seven minutes and 21 seconds, establishing a new business jet "time-to-climb" record.

December 30, 1965—Lear Jet Avionics Division headquarters is established in Grand Rapids, Michigan.

February 1, 1966—A third major expansion in Wichita adds a customer aircraft service center, bringing total square footage to 400,000.

February 24, 1966—First flight of Model 24.

March 17, 1966—Model 24 awarded FAA type certificate; first business aircraft to ever be certificated under FAR Part 25, the new air transport category which set standards for all commercial jet transports, including the 747, DC-10 and L-1011.

April 23, 1966—Third fatal Learjet crash in Texas.

May 23-26, 1966—A standard Model 24 circles the earth in flying time of 50 hours and 20 minutes.

August 12, 1966—First flight of Model 25.

September 19, 1966—Lear Jet Corporation name changed to Lear Jet Industries, Inc.

April 10, 1967—Gates Rubber Company acquires controlling interest in Lear Jet Industries, Inc.

October 10, 1967—Model 25 awarded FAA type certificate.

February 20, 1968—A standard production Model 25 flies to 40,000 feet in six minutes, 19 seconds, surpassing the former "time-to-climb" record set by the Model 23.

May 1, 1968—The Avionics Division becomes Jet Electronics & Technology, Inc. (J.E.T.), a wholly owned subsidiary, in Grand Rapids, Michigan.

May 23, 1968—Lear Jet acquires Avsco, Inc., a leading producer of plastic products.

June 1, 1968—A new Learjet service center begins operation in Wichita, doubling the previous size.

September 25, 1968—The company announces the Model 24B.

October 1, 1968—The Stereo Division becomes a subsidiary of Lear Jet Industries, Inc., becoming known as Lear Jet Stereo, Inc.

December 17, 1968—Model 24B awarded an FAA type certificate.

February 7, 1969—First sales of the Model 25 outside the United States are announced.

April 2, 1969—William P. Lear, Sr. resigns as Lear Jet Industries board member.

December 2, 1969—Shareholders of Lear Jet Industries, Inc. agree to make Gates Aviation a wholly owned subsidiary of Lear Jet Industries.

December 2, 1969—Corporate name is changed from Lear Jet Industries, Inc. to Gates Learjet Corporation.

May 5, 1970—FAA approves category II operations for properly equipped Learjets.

July 17, 1970—FAA certificates Model 24D, which replaces the Model 24B.

August 30, 1970—Model 25C sets a new round-trip speed record for all classes of commercial aircraft by flying nonstop from Los Angeles to New York, refueling, and then returning in 11 hours and 23 minutes.

September 4, 1970—Models 25B and 25C awarded FAA type certificates.

October 16, 1970—G.H.B. "Hig" Gould is named president of Gates Learjet Corporation, replacing Charles C. Gates, who remains chairman.

January 1, 1971—Learjet deliveries in 1970 were near 300, marking the sixth year in a row that Learjet leads all business jet manufacturers in total production.

February 28, 1971—Model 25C makes a nonstop 2,720-mile flight from Wichita to Caracas, Venezuela, in five hours and 30 minutes.

April 30, 1971—Charles C. Gates resumes the duties of president of Gates Learjet Corporation following the April 23rd death of G.H.B. Gould.

May 1, 1971—Gates Learjet Corporation is reorganized around only aircraft-oriented operations. Lear Jet Stereo, Inc., Avsco, Inc., and the Static Power Division are absorbed by the Gates Rubber Company, leaving Gates Learjet with aircraft manufacture, marketing, and service functions; Jet Electronics & Technology, Inc. remains as a subsidiary.

May 19, 1971—First flight of TFE-731-2 turbofan-powered Model 25.

October 6, 1971—Presidential "E" award is presented Gates Learjet by U.S. Department of Commerce for company's performance in export sales.

October 7, 1971—Harry B. Combs, Gates Learjet board member and former chairman of Gates Aviation Corporation, is elected president of Gates Learjet Corporation.

January 6, 1972—FlightSafety International, Inc. establishes a training center at Gates Learjet facilities in Wichita for pilot and maintenance ground school.

January 11, 1972—Learjet receives FAA certification authorizing operation from gravel runways.

June 26, 1972—A record net profit is reported by Gates Learjet Corporation for fiscal year 1972, climaxing a dramatic financial turnaround.

January 7, 1973—Tenth anniversary of the Learjet factory opening is observed with the delivery of 360th aircraft.

February 20, 1973—Gates Learjet's three fixed-base operations are consolidated under the name Combs Gates.

June 30, 1973—A record 90 purchase orders for Learjets were received during fiscal year 1973.

August 22, 1973—First flight of the Model 35.

August 28, 1973—Models 35 and 36 are unveiled at Wichita.

October 8, 1973—Gates Learjet delivers its 400th aircraft, a Model 25B, to Fischer Industries of Cleveland.

July 5, 1974—Models 25B and 25C are issued British Type Certificates.

July 9, 1974—Models 35 and 36 receive FAA type certification.

September 1, 1974—Learjet fleet tops the 1,000,000-flight-hour mark.

December 11, 1974—Mesa Petroleum Co. of Amarillo becomes first corporate owner of a Model 35/36 series aircraft.

January 1, 1975—Gates Learjet leads the business jet industry in total aircraft delivered for the tenth consecutive year, with a total of 479 Learjets delivered.

April 5, 1975—A standard-equipped Model 36 flies nonstop 3,833 miles from Hawaii to Wichita in seven hours and 15 minutes.

April 8, 1975—The 500th Learjet, a 24D, is delivered to the Navy of Mexico.

October 27, 1975—Century III series Models 24E and 24F are announced by Gates Learjet.

December 20, 1975—Groundbreaking ceremonies are held for a new facility at Tucson International Airport.

January 1, 1976—Total Learjet deliveries (through 1975) reach 570.

May 1, 1976—A record 93 new Learjets delivered during the fiscal year just ended.

May 17-19, 1976—A Model 36, piloted by golfer-businessman-pilot Arnold Palmer, flies around the world in 57 hours, 26 minutes.

June 15, 1976—Gates Learjet completion center opens in Tucson.

August 2, 1976—The FAA announces certification of the last of six new Century III series Learjet models.

January 1, 1977—Gates Learjet marks its 12th consecutive year as the industry leader, having delivered a total of 655 aircraft since 1964.

April 15, 1977—For Learjet 24E/F and 25D/F, FAA approves flight operations to 51,000 feet, highest level ever achieved in U.S. civil aviation.

June 15, 1977—Gates Learjet delivers its 700th aircraft, a Model 35A, to Chrysler Corporation.

August 24, 1977—First flight of the Model 28.

September 26, 1977—The Longhorn series is unveiled with the flight of a Model 28 at Houston, the day before the opening of the National Business Aircraft Association annual meeting.

January 1, 1978—The delivery of 105 Learjets in calendar year 1977 establishes an industry record and increases to 760 the total number of Learjets delivered.

April 1, 1978—The second Learjet built, a Model 23, goes on exhibit at the Smithsonian Institution's National Air and Space Museum in Washington, D.C.

April 1, 1978—A 44,000-square-foot customer service center is completed at Gates Learjet's Tucson facility.

April 26, 1978—A Model 36A is delivered to Mollers Maschinenfabrik of Beckum, West Germany, marking Gates Learjet's 800th delivery.

May 14, 1978—William P. Lear, Sr. dies.

August 3, 1978—A Model 23 becomes the first Learjet to reach 10,000 hours flight time.

August 30, 1978—A special mission Model 35A is developed for sea patrol work.

November 1, 1978—FlightSafety International establishes a 10,000-square-foot Learjet training center at Gates Learjet's Tucson facility.

January 1, 1979—Gates Learjet delivers 102 airplanes in 1978, with 862 total aircraft delivered to date.

January 29, 1979—Models 28 and 29 are awarded FAA type certificates.

February 2, 1979—First flying prototype of the Model 50 series rolls off the assembly line in Wichita.

February 21, 1979—Former astronaut Neil A. Armstrong breaks five world records for business jets at Kitty Hawk, North Carolina, when his Model 28 climbs above 50,000 feet in a little over 12 minutes.

April 19, 1979—First flight of Model 54/55/56 series.

April 27, 1979—Gates Learjet's 900th aircraft, a Model 35A, is delivered to McDonnell Douglas Corporation of St. Louis.

October 4, 1979—An advanced handling package, called Softflite, to improve Learjet stall characteristics receives FAA certification for Model 24s.

February 22, 1980—President Harry B. Combs announces a 200,000-square-foot expansion of customer service facilities.

March 28, 1980—Rollout of first production Model 50 series Learjet.

December 2, 1980—Finland's Air Force purchases three Learjets fitted for special missions.

January 1, 1981—Gates Learjet delivers 120 new Learjets in 1980, with over 1,000 Learjets now in service worldwide.

March 18, 1981—Learjet Model 55 receives FAA certification.

April 30, 1981—Ceremonies are held in Tucson to deliver the first Model 55 production aircraft to Transcontinental Gas Pipe Line Corporation, Houston.

June 5, 1981—Gates Learjet announces record international deliveries of 40 new aircraft, valued at more than $100 million, during calendar year 1980.

January 6, 1982—Gates Learjet delivers 138 new Learjets in 1981, with more than 1,220 Learjets in service worldwide.

May 11, 1982—Charles C. Gates, chairman of the board, announces the election of Harry B. Combs as vice chairman of Gates Learjet Corporation.

May 11, 1982—Bermar S. "Bib" Stillwell is elected president of Gates Learjet Corporation and subsequently to the company's board of directors.

May 18, 1982—Gates Learjet announces the addition of five new service facilities, bringing the number of official facilities to 27.

June 7, 1982—Combs Gates, Inc., Gates Learjet's sales and service subsidiary, purchases Air-Kaman at Bradley International Airport, Windsor Locks, Connecticut.

June 9-18, 1982—First production Model 25G enters demonstration service, breaking long-distance speed and fuel consumption records.

September 10, 1982—Defense Forces of Finland receive first of three new special mission Model 35As in ceremonies at Wichita plant.

January 25, 1983—Government of Canada certificates the Model 55.

February 16-18, 1983—A Model 35A, piloted by businesswoman-pilot Brooke Knapp, sets around-the-world speed record of 50 hours, 22 minutes, and 42 seconds total elapsed time.

March 9, 1983—FAA certifies Model 55ER, the first in a planned series of extended-range versions of the Model 55.

May 26, 1983—Gates Learjet announces it has signed a contract with the People's Republic of China for delivery of new Model 30 series aircraft equipped with side-looking airborne radar (SLAR).

May 26, 1983—FAA certifies the Model 55LR.

May 26, 1983—A Model 55LR establishes a world speed record, flying from Los Angeles to Paris in a total elapsed time of 12 hours, 37 minutes, 40 seconds, which includes a 19-minute fuel stop at Bangor, Maine.

June 6, 1983—On the return flight from Paris to Los Angeles, the Model 55LR sets a record total elapsed time of 14 hours, 36 minutes, 42 seconds, including a 17-minute, 40-second fuel stop at Halifax, Nova Scotia.

July 7, 1983—A standard production Model 55 breaks six previous world records in the time-to-climb and altitude categories for business aircraft in its weight class.

July 22, 1983—Comb Gates, Inc., a Gates Learjet subsidiary, opens a newly completed 44,000 square foot complex at the Fort Lauderdale/Hollywood International Airport.

September 19, 1983—The Department of Defense awards Gates Learjet a $175,403,178 fixed-price lease and contractor logistic support contract to supply and support 80 Model 35As for the U.S. Air Force's Operational Support Aircraft program.

September 28, 1983—The FAA certifies Softflite I, a wing modification developed for Models 23 and 24.

December 7, 1983—Rollout ceremony at the Gates Learjet Tucson facility commemorates the 100th Model 55 manufactured.

February 23, 1984—Gates Learjet Aircraft Services Corporation (GLASCO) is formed as a wholly owned subsidiary to support U.S.A.F. C-21A Learjets.

March 13, 1984—Gates Learjet rolls out the first of 80 new C-21A operational support aircraft, six months after the lease contract was signed.

April 10, 1984—Gates Learjet delivers the 100th Model 55 to United Telecommunications of Kansas City.

April 20, 1984—A 36A is the first Learjet delivered to the People's Republic of China.

July 11, 1984—Gates Learjet announces startup of a high technology Aerospace Division in Wichita.

September 3, 1984—The FAA certifies the Marquardt MTR-101 target launch and recovery tow reel for the Learjet.

October 1, 1984—Gates Learjet unveils the first of the new Model 55s, featuring numerous performance improvements.

October 13, 1984—Gates Learjet celebrates the 20th anniversary of the first production Learjet delivery.

March 19, 1985—Model 55 is certified for a 10-passenger configuration.

April 8, 1985—The U.S. Air Force C-21A marks its first service anniversary with 52 aircraft delivered on or ahead of schedule.

June 17, 1985—James B. Taylor is elected president and chief executive officer of Gates Learjet Corporation following the resignation of B. S. Stillwell.

September 10, 1985—Gates Learjet's Aerospace Division is selected by Martin Marietta Corporation to build intertank panels and a support beam for the Space Shuttle's main booster rocket.

October 23, 1985—The 80th and final C-21A is delivered on schedule to the U.S. Air Force.

January 9, 1986—First Model U36A, a modified commercial Model 36A, is delivered to the Japan Maritime Self-Defense Force.

February 21, 1986—Corporate headquarters is relocated to Tucson from Wichita.

September 30, 1986—Gates Learjet and the U.S. Air Force reach an agreement on the purchase of a fleet of C-21As for $180 million.

September 30, 1986—Model 55B is unveiled at the National Business Aircraft Association annual meeting in Anaheim.

December 12, 1986—Brazilian Air Force signs a contract for three Model 35A special missions aircraft.

December 23, 1986—BF Goodrich Company acquires Gates Learjet's subsidiary, Jet Electronics & Technology, Inc.

January 15, 1987—Second Model U36A, a modified commercial 36A, is delivered to the Japan Maritime Self-Defense Force.

January 28, 1987—For the first time, customer service is expanded to accommodate modification on aircraft other than Learjets.

August 3, 1987—U.S. Air Force signs a contract for four C-21A aircraft for the Air National Guard.

August 5, 1987—Gates Corporation announces a definitive agreement to sell its 64.8 percent interest in Gates Learjet to Integrated Acquisition, Inc., a wholly owned subsidiary of Integrated Resources, Inc. of New York.

August 25, 1987—Royal Thai Air Force signs a contract for two Model 35A special missions aircraft.

September 9, 1987—Integrated Acquisition, Inc. completes acquisition of 64.8 percent interest in Gates Learjet from the Gates Corporation.

September 11, 1987—Integrated Acquisition, Inc. announces a restructuring of Gates Learjet's board of directors.

September 25, 1987—The company's Aerospace Division delivers the first Space Shuttle parts to the Martin Marietta Corporation.

September 29, 1987—Models 31 and 55C are unveiled at the National Business Aircraft Association meeting in New Orleans.

October 23, 1987—Integrated Acquisition announces it has acquired 96.1 percent of the shares of Learjet common stock.

October 30, 1987—Integrated Acquisition announces it has consummated its acquisition of Gates Learjet Corporation, now a privately held company.

November 27, 1987—Brazilian Air Force signs a contract for three additional Learjet 35As.

January 21, 1988—Beverly N. Lancaster is named president and chief executive officer, succeeding James B. Taylor.

February 2, 1988—For economic reasons, Learjet decides to consolidate all manufacturing operations and corporate offices in Wichita.

April 4, 1988—Name of Gates Learjet Corporation is changed to Learjet Corporation.

April 25, 1988—AMR Services Corp. (a unit of American Airlines) signs an agreement with Integrated Acquisitions to acquire the Combs Gates Denver chain of fixed base operations.

June 30, 1988—AMR Services Corp. completes acquisition of Combs Gates Denver.

August 1, 1988—FAA certification of Model 31.

January 1, 1989—Learjet Corporation completes move of all aircraft production from Tucson to Wichita, leaving the modification center, customer service and marketing offices at the Arizona location.

March 1, 1989—Brian E. Barents elected president of Learjet Corporation. Bev Lancaster elected Chairman and chief executive officer.

Postscript

In February of 1990, Learjet lost the TTTS competition to a team led by Beech Aircraft. Unrelated to this event, Learjet's parent, Integrated Resources, Inc., sought to sell the Learjet subsidiary months earlier. Following months of speculation and negotiation with several possible suitors, Bomardier Inc. of Montreal emerged as the purchaser of Learjet Corporation in May of 1990.

Bomardier is a leading worldwide manufacturer of transportation equipment: rail transit equipment, urban, suburban and intercity vehicles, snowmobiles, and personal watercraft. In civil and military aerospace, its Canadair Group produces the wide-body Challenger business jet (which Bill Lear had so vehemently protested), the CL-215 amphibian, airframe components for other aircraft manufacturers, and unmanned airborne surveillance systems. Bomardier's Northern Ireland subsidiary, Short Brothers (Shorts), produces civil and military aircraft and aerostructures, as well as close-air defense missiles.

Index